Dublin
Express

for Celine !

Dublin
Express

Colin Bateman

Dublin Express Copyright © Colin Bateman 2013

A Bateman Book
c/o 12 Farnham Road
Bangor
N. Ireland BT20 3SP

www.colinbateman.com

A CIP catalogue reference for this book is available from the British Library

ISBN 978-0-9926424-0-2

Typeset by Freight in Garamond
Printed and bound by Bell and Bain, Glasgow

Thanks

The publication of Dublin Express has been funded through a kickstarter crowd funding campaign. I am eternally grateful to those listed below who supported the venture.

My thanks to: *Curtis Brown Literary Agency*, Kirsty Barr, Suzanne, Eoin Colfer, Gillian Thurley, Kyle Spence, Jackie Colville, Stephen Burnside, Gail McCartney, Mark Larmour, Nick Williams, Eunan McAteer, Mary-Ann Orr, Ryan Harkness, Marc Wydler, Shaun Wright, Geoff Rooney, David Chantrey, Jeremy Lilburn, Graeme Scarfe, Matt Hanlon, Gareth McNamara, Natasha Anne Thompson, Elisabeth Marie Mouchard, Malcolm Bannon, Mark Burton, Ed Wood, Alan Murray, Peadar Coll, Laura Mousseau, Emma Browning, Susan Bowles, Liz D'Arcy, Kirsty Barr, Adam Davison, Jo Burgess, Adam Duff, Gregory McCausland, Lee Cook, Helen Parry, Nicky Haines, Tom Croft, Gavin Sutter, Chris Caldwell, Pamela Dennison, Daniel Gregorious, Brendan O'Mahony, Alan Close, David Hughes, Michael Delaney, Jacquie Cassidy, Karen McMaster, Colette Sunner , Bill Badger, Paul Marshall, Neville Carvill, Thomas O'Shea, Zane Radcliffe, Simon Olney, Rachel Anderson, Elizabeth Loughran.

Contents:

Preface

I've never *volunteered* to write a short story – they're much too hard work.

Many people, when they start out writing, their first bash is usually at a short story. This is because it seems like the easier option. Short stories are, by definition, *shorter* than a novel, or a play, or a screenplay. (Don't get me started on poetry.) Short stories are *not* the easy option. They are notoriously difficult to get right. I'm not claiming that any of the stories collected here are right, but someone liked them enough to publish them and to even pay me for them, though anyone who gets rewarded with more than a jar of jam and a *Twix* for writing a short story is doing rather well.

The title story, *Dublin Express*, originally appeared in the Dublin edition of Maxim Jakubowski's anthology series of erotic fiction, *Sex in the City*. I was very surprised when he accepted it as it doesn't really have any erotic content. It's very much a *what if* story. So much of our history is down to chance and luck, bad or good.

The second story, *Unhappy Endings*, was a direct commission for *Red Bull* magazine. Yep, no *New Yorker* or *Granta* for me. I hope it's dark and funny and disturbing. It was selected for *The Mammoth Book of Best British Crime*, which is a bit like *The Penguin Book of Best British Crime* but with, er, mammoths.

NIPD Blue was my first published short story, appearing in 1998's *Mean Time* anthology edited by Jerry Sykes. I also used it as the basis of a short film I directed a year later, *The Devil You Know*, which was shown at the Edinburgh Film Festival and on BBC 2.

Some readers might recognise *The Case of Mrs Geary's Leather Trousers*, as with relatively few changes it also forms the opening chapters of my 2009 novel *Mystery Man*. But the short story had been around since 2004 when I was due to launch my novel *Driving Big Davie* in Belfast mystery book shop No Alibis. I couldn't quite bring myself to read the opening chapter of my novel, as I usually do at book launches, because it was essentially all about masturbation, so I was forced over the course of a weekend to come up with something I could read instead. *Mrs Geary* is mostly set in this very real book shop, but with a completely fictitious owner acting up as private eye. He has subsequently appeared in three further novels.

The Prize, which deals with an 'ex' terrorist bringing his old skills into play as he attempts to conquer the art world, was commissioned by BBC Radio 4 and recorded live at the Belfast Festival. It was memorably read by actor Adrian Dunbar. It was supposed to be something of a spoof of the art world's top award, The Turner Prize. BBC producers wouldn't allow me to call it that, so I fooled everyone by renaming it The Learner Prize. Parts of it were later extensively re-written for my 2005 novel, *Belfast Confidential*.

Nothing goes to waste!

The second part of this book is taken up with my first stage play, *National Anthem*, which was brought to the stage through Ransom Productions and commissioned through the Belfast Festival in 2010. It's about a under achieving poet and an egotistical composer being commissioned at a very late stage to write a new national anthem for Northern Ireland.

I have to say that having my play on stage at the Baby Grand (the smaller theatre in the Grand Opera House) was one of the best writing experiences I have had – the play sold out its two week run during the festival and then toured Northern Ireland to equally packed venues. It was also short listed for Best New Play at the Irish Theatre Awards. I think it represents some of my best writing, because if something doesn't work on stage it quickly becomes clear, and continues to be wrong night, after night, after night, until you fix it. There is no hiding place on a stage.

Dublin Express

Danny Guthrie said, 'Excuse me, is this seat taken?'

Her eyes flitted up. Dark hair, pale skin, reddish tinge, maybe twenty, college books out on the table, ipod earphones and the tsk-tsk of her music. This train, the Dublin train, was far from packed. It was mid-morning, Spring. He'd gotten on at Drogheda and patrolled up and down the corridor until he spotted her.

She didn't really say yes or no, just nodded, which could have meant anything. But he sat and she returned her attention to her books. He tried to read them upside down.

He said, 'French?'

She said, 'What?' and pulled out one of her earphones.

'Studying French?' She nodded. Before she could put it back in he said, 'You must have exams coming up, studying on a Saturday.'

'Yeah. Soon.' She replaced the earphone. Her cheeks were a little redder. She was easily embarrassed.

'That's good,' he said. 'If it needs done.'

She looked up. 'Sorry?' She pulled the earphone out again.

'Sorry, didn't mean to disturb you.'

'No, it's okay.' It clearly *wasn't* okay, but now she felt she couldn't just go back to the music. 'What were you saying?'

'Nothing, really. Just – French, it's a beautiful language.'

'Oh. Do you...?'

'Oui.'

He smiled, and she smiled, getting it. He was a bit older than her, short black hair, hint of stubble. Neat.

'You going into town?' he asked.

Stupid question, just for the sake of it really. Of course she was going into town. The train was going into town, it was an express, no other stops between Drogheda and town.

'Oh – yeah. Yeah. Meeting my boyfriend.'

Making a point. *Boyfriend*. When he held her gaze she managed a half smile, then looked away. Banks of unsold apartments slid past. He watched them as well.

Then she said, 'You?'

'Yeah. Into town. Something to do. *Man on a mission*.'

'Mysterious.'

'Yeah, kinda.'

'You could tell me, but then you'd have to kill me?'

But he didn't smile back the way she expected, just kept looking at her. She felt a bit foolish and averted her eyes. She didn't know him from Adam. He could easily be a nutter. She looked up, and *now* he was smiling. He was full of himself. She quite liked that, in a man.

Danny Guthrie said, 'You're not going to see the President?'

'The President?'

'Yeah. She's giving a speech out at the Barracks, anniversary of something or other.'

'No. No interest.'

'Funny that, isn't it? If it was the President of like, America, there'd be motorcades and Secret Service and all that shit, but with her, you know, she'll be lucky if there's a traffic warden and a Guard with a dodgy walkie-talkie. President of our own country, nobody gives a toss.'

'Yeah, yeah, I suppose. But I mean, she's ceremonial more than... you know? She doesn't have her finger on the nuclear button or anything.'

'Yeah, I suppose. I'm going to pop out anyway, have a listen.'

'Really?'

'Sure. Like I said. *Man on a mission*.'

This time he patted his jacket.

She gave a little laugh, but at the same time her brow furrowed. She patted her own top, like what's the big secret? But he just kept looking at her. She pretended to return her attention to her books. Without quite looking up she was aware that he was closer, arms folded, on the table, leaning towards her.

Danny Guthrie said: 'Do you think if someone has the chance to alter the course of history, for the good, they should?'

'I'm sorry?'

'Do you…I mean, look you're studying French, right? Say if a couple of hundred years ago someone, say a waiter, had had the foresight to whisper in Napoleon's ear that invading Russia was really going to fuck him up, and in so whispering, and Napoleon taking it on board, he saved the lives of hundreds of thousands of soldiers, do you think you would have whispered, if you were a waiter, waitress, or would you have said, these big world events have nothing to do with me, I just serve frog's legs and shit?'

'If I was a just a waitress, how would I even know what could happen during a Russian campaign?'

'Well, for one, I think you're needlessly complicating this, but for the sake of argument, you're a waitress whose family came from Russia, and you know how bloody cold the winters are, which a lot of people in France at the time must have known too but were too scared to say, at least until you came along. But my point is, do you think you would have said something?'

'Well, I'd like to think so.'

'Okay, but what if we took it one step further. Say Lee Harvey Oswald…'

'Lee Harvey Oswald,' she said quickly.

He started to look exasperated, but it was halted by her sudden, radiant smile. 'Sorry,' she said.

It was good that she was more relaxed with him now, bearing in mind what was coming.

'You know the story, okay? He was in the Book Depository. But say he was getting set up to shoot Kennedy, and you happened to walk in and say, 'Lee Harvey Oswald, what do you think you're doing?' And he said he was going to shoot the President because of the Bay of Pigs and the Mafia, or whatever, but now you knew what he was planning, so he was going to have to kill you, and you knew it too, and he knew that you knew it, so you had a choice to make. You could either run for it, which wasn't going to work, or start screaming, but who was going to hear you way up there with all the noise outside, waiting for the President? So what would you do, you wanted to save your own life, and you wanted to save the President's, what really would you do?'

'I...don't know.'

'What have you got to bargain with?'

'I don't...I'm not sure what you mean.'

'There's this guy in front of you, he's like an ex-marine or something, so he's built, but he's also a bit nerdy looking, and you, you're this young girl, young beautiful student, how're you going to distract him, save the President, maybe save the world, because there's fingers on nuclear buttons could easily press fire if Kennedy goes down. What're you going to do?'

'I don't really...'

'Would you do it?'

'Would I do what?'

'Would you say to Lee Harvey Oswald, on the verge of maybe destroying civilisation as we know it, would you say, Lee Harvey, you can make love to me right now, if only you won't do this terrible thing, and afterwards I promise I won't even tell a single person what you were up to.'

'You mean would I have sex with him?'

'To save the world.'

'I don't know. God. Why would you ever ask such a...Yes. Maybe. To save the world.' She was very flushed now. 'He'd have to wear a condom.'

Danny Guthrie said, 'What if that was a deal breaker?'

'Wearing a condom?'

'Yes, what if he had a strict no condoms rule?'

'Well, yes, maybe to save the world. God. How did we start talking about this? We're nearly in town.'

'It's just interesting, isn't it? So, if you'll forgive my French, if we zipped back forty, fifty years, to save the President, Camelot, all that bollocks, you would screw Lee Harvey Oswald on the floor of the Texas Book Depository.'

'The floor?'

'Yes. The floor.'

'I suppose. To save the world.'

'Okay then, obvious next question. Say the equivalent of Lee Harvey Oswald, a Twenty First Century Lee Harvey, got on this train, and he was on his way to assassinate, say, the President of Ireland, what would you do to save her?'

'Well it's hardly the same thing, is it?'

'Okay, granted, no it's not. Obviously she hasn't got that same standing. Nobody hangs on her every word. But for the sake of argument. If you could save her life, what would you do? If someone who got on a train and sat down beside you and said they were going to shoot the President of Ireland, but might not if you agreed to ride them in the toilets.'

'Ride...?! No, definitely not.'

'Not just to save the life of the President of this country, but to save the life of a person. Of a *woman*.'

'*No.*'

'No? Why not?'

'Because doing that and saving the world, there's a big difference between that and saving one person. Horrible choice as it is, I wouldn't.'

'What would you do?'

'In what sense?'

'In a sexual sense.'

'To save the President of Ireland what would I do in a sexual sense?'

'Yes.' He patted his jacket. 'If he, the lunatic with the gun in his coat said to you, show me one of your breasts right here, right now, and I won't take the head off the President of this green and pleasant land, would you do it?'

'Do you have a gun in your jacket?'

'Oh, we're talking about me now, are we? Are you sure about that? And if we are, do I have a gun? Well, that's for you to decide.'

'One breast for the life of the President? I would have to think about it.'

'Maybe you wouldn't have much time to think.'

'Maybe you don't have a gun.'

'Maybe I do.'

'Maybe you wouldn't get close enough to kill her. If you have a gun it has to be small other wise I'd see it, so it's not like your Lee Harvey with his sniper's rifle or whatever he had. So maybe you're not as big a threat as you think you are.'

'Or maybe I am. Maybe I have military training and know all about close quarter combat, take her eye out soon as look at her. Or maybe that's the chance you have to take. Save the President's life by showing me a breast. It doesn't seem like such a big sacrifice. Really.'

'It's not about the sacrifice.'

'What is it about then?'

'It's about you, a complete stranger, trying to pressure me. For all I know you do this every week, every day, maybe you've seen every tit north of Dublin.'

'For all you know, maybe I have. It doesn't change your predicament. So what's it going to be, are you going to show me your breast?'

'Are you going to show me your gun?'

'That's not how we play this. You have to decide if it's worth the gamble. I may have a gun, I may not. But you definitely have a breast. And it's whether you think it's worth showing it, knowing that by so doing there's a chance that you might be saving the President's life.'

'And an equal chance of me being suckered in by a frickin' chancer.'

The doors hissed and the conductor appeared. He said, 'Tickets please,' to the couple three seats back.

Danny Guthrie said, 'If you say anything to him, I'll kill him too.'

'If you have a gun.'

'Your call.'

He came to their facing seats and said, 'Tickets.'
She held Danny Guthrie's eyes, and held out her ticket.

Danny Guthrie kept looking at her.

The conductor said, 'Sir?'

Danny Guthrie nodded. But didn't take his eyes off her. He unzipped his jacket enough to remove his wallet from an inside pocket. He slipped out a note without looking at it. The conductor ran off a ticket and handed it to him with the change.

Danny Guthrie said, 'Thank you.'

The conductor moved on. Only when he was gone did Danny Guthrie put the ticket, wallet and change back into his pocket, but this time he opened the jacket a little wider and she thought she saw, she was nearly sure she thought she saw, she was about fifty-fifty that she thought she saw the dark outline of something that might or might not have been the butt of a gun.

'So what's it to be?' asked Danny Guthrie.

****

Two hours later she was naked and exhausted in her boyfriend's bed, in his apartment, first floor, curtains open, the canal beyond. The sun was streaming through the window. She had bruises on her knees from making love on the hardwood floor. She had scrapes on her back from making love against the plumbing in the bathroom.

The boyfriend was saying, 'You're confusing me. You're quite the tiger, but every twenty minutes you jump up to check the news. Is there something going on I should know about?'

'No, nothing...just curious.'

He pulled her too him. He kissed her hard.

And then in the silence of another kiss, she heard:

'We interrupt this programme for an important news flash. We cross now to...'

Unhappy Endings

I say yes to a lot of things I shouldn't really say yes to, like the writing of this short story. It's worth about a grand, but out of that there's an agent to pay and a few pounds whittled away on research. It'll appear under a pseudonym, nobody will ever connect me to it; it's quite liberating, actually, I don't have to worry about what critics think or my literary reputation and I can just indulge in flights of fancy or get away with murder or generally just please myself. The problem is that there's always an unhappy ending, and that depresses me. Not at the time, you understand, but later. I just have a thing about writing unhappy endings.

My research isn't much more than sitting in the pub having a few pints watching and listening, because I'm not really one for learning the intricate details of anything. If there's brain surgery in my story, I don't feel the need to talk to a brain surgeon. I look it up on the net, give it a cursory read and then wing it. If you crash landed on a desert island and the pilot had a fractured skull and you had to operate to save his life so that he could, after a substantial period of recovery and perhaps physiotherapy and rehabilitation, together with the frequent consumption of the milk of coconuts, somehow repair the plane and fly you out of there, you wouldn't want to use my story as a guide to how to drill into his head to relieve the pressure or take out the blood clot, because you'd really mess him up. He'd be slobbering in a wheelchair for the rest of his life, pointing the finger of blame at me, though of course he wouldn't be able to literally point the finger of blame at me because well, you would have drilled into the area of the brain that controls the finger of blame. On my advice you would also have used the corkscrew you rescued from the premier seats at the front to do the drilling, pausing only to comment sardonically that planes don't reverse into crashes and they should have the rich seats at the back. Actually using the corkscrew would be pretty damn sore unless you improvised chloroform using a mixture of vodka, egg whites and broccoli. You can't really improvise chloroform using vodka, egg whites and broccoli. Don't try it at home, because it's really difficult to get the right kind of broccoli. You need Spanish broccoli, grown in the foot hills of the Andes. You see, when information is presented in fiction you have a tendency to accept it as fact just because it's there on the page before you; you presume we've done the research. Think about it. The Andes aren't in Spain, but you just blithely accepted that they were.

This story features a woman who works in a bank. She could work *anywhere* because it's not really relevant, but having her work in a bank adds a certain *je ne sais quoi* given what later develops with the banknotes. I can toss in *je ne sais quoi* because it's French everyone understands. I don't speak French. If I made her a French banker I'd really be screwed because even though the story would be in English, you'd expect her to come out with a couple of French words just to make her character seem kosher. A French Jew, in fact. She's from Montmartrelle, I might say, which shows that I can look up a map of Paris, and then corrupt not only the specific area but the entire *arrondissement* just enough to make it appear like it's really based on Montmartre and I've changed it subtly because what I'm writing is too damn close to the truth to allow me to use its real name. What I'm writing must be closer to *roman a clef* than fiction, which also adds a certain *frisson* which will be further advanced by the pointless and distracting use of *italics*. All of which will be entirely irrelevant, because she's not a French Jewess from Montmartrelle, but a banker from Derby.

The hotel bar is modern with a pale wooden floor. You would think it would stain, but it can be wiped clean with a damp sponge. The ambience is provided by Sky Sports News with the sound high enough to be distracting but low enough not to impart any information, and the screen is just far enough away from where I'm sitting to prevent me from accurately reading the tickertape information at the bottom or the league tables and fixtures at the side. Sky Sports News is thus failing to inform me of anything on several different levels. The situation could be rectified if I simply moved closer, but I've become captivated by the Derby woman having a heart to heart with her boyfriend. I never actually see her boyfriend's face because they're both hidden by a pillar, and I don't hear anything he says because he's quietly spoken, but I hear everything she says because she's louder, and I'm drawn to her because I was once engaged to a woman who said she came from Derby. I killed that woman because she tried to break it off. When the Jehovah's Witnesses came to the door shortly afterwards, I still had blood and soil on my hands. They asked to speak to the woman from Derby, with whom they clearly had already established some kind of relationship, or she must have at least hinted at some stage that she might be willing to let them in, which is a dangerous thing to do with Jehovah's Witnesses, or Mormons, or insurance salesmen, because they're like multiple dogs with multiple bones, but I told them that I had just murdered her and buried her under the patio. People will accept anything if you present it in the right way. They laughed politely and left, no doubt discussing my unusual sense of humour, and I was able to make a clean getaway, that time, even though I would have been quite intrigued to discover if Jehovah's Witnesses actually made for good witnesses.

It takes a lot of work to dig up a patio.

It's useful to have a power point near by.

I catch a glimpse of the guy leaving. When I peer around the pillar and ask her if she's okay, because she's sobbing, she says there was no need for him to storm off like that. For the purposes of this story, she is good looking. If she was some big thunder-thighed porpoise, what follows would feel rather sordid, and you would probably allow it to colour your perceptions of me as a person. It is a universal truth that people prefer to read about attractive people making love, because you can understand the animal passions they might arouse in each other. If she had thick ankles and sagging arms and skin like a peppered mackerel, then it would just read as if I was taking advantage of her despair. So for the purposes of this story she is attractive. We are both, in fact, attractive. In fact, I'm gorgeous. Also, it would probably work better if it was set in Montmartrelle, with the bells of the Eiffel Tower peeling softly in the background, but for the purposes of this story the location will remain firmly here, in this dull city. But don't worry, she is not another one who ends up under the patio. That would be ridiculous. Her room is on the nineteenth floor of this hotel, up where there are no patios.

In retrospect, I will remove the bells from the Eiffel Tower. I could only justify them by creating an alternative history for France in general and the Tower in particular, one in which Napoleon wasn't defeated at Waterloo etc. etc. and I would have to continue you right up to the modern era and actually make her a French banker, but this is a short story and they're paying by the word, and it's really not worth the effort.

I get into her room by telling her the story about the man who won the lottery. It always works. He was an ugly man who very occasionally had ugly girlfriends, which is another universal truth. But when he won the lottery he decided that now he was entitled to enjoy the company of the most beautiful woman in the world. He found her in a hotel just like this one, I say. He watched her all night, and she too had had a row with her boyfriend, and he too had stormed off leaving her without any money of her own, which was ironic, because she worked in a bank.

It wasn't really ironic, but I was playing my game.

'I work in a bank too!' my lady cries.

'Really? What a coincidence. Anyway, the woman in my ugly lottery man story wanted to stay out and have a good time, but now she was going to have to go back to her room all by her lonely self and cry. Except, this ugly lottery guy sidles up to her and says, you don't normally talk to guys like me, and you'll probably slap me in the face, but today I became richer than I ever thought I could be, and I want to do something really special, I want to make love to you. He told her she was the most beautiful woman he had ever seen and that he knew that under normal circumstances she would never look even once at him, but he had seen her being abandoned by her man, and observed her checking her purse for money she did not have, and now he wanted to make her an offer. He told her he had thirty thousand pounds in cash in his jacket and that he would give her all of it in exchange for one hour in bed with her.

Her first instinct, naturally, was to call security, but she hesitated, and she started to think about how awful her boyfriend was to leave her like that, even though she still loved him, and how much thirty thousand was, and how nobody would ever have to know what she'd done for it; she could say that she had won the lottery, and in some ways she had.

And I pause there and take a sip of my drink.

'Well, did she do it, did she?'

The Derby woman is well and truly sucked in.

I nod.

'Oh, the little...and did she...did she enjoy it? You know what they say about ugly men. Did she fall in love and...?'

'She hated it. He did all sorts of despicable things to her, but she didn't think she could protest. She kept thinking of the money.'

'And I'll bet he ran off without paying her!'

'No. He paid her. Thirty thousand. And an extra five for her tears. But before he handed it over, and when he was still lying on top of her, he said, just one more thing. Kiss me and this time use your tongue.'

She hadn't used it at all. She was keeping it for her boyfriend. Using her tongue somehow seemed more intimate than any of the unspeakable acts she had so recently partaken of.

I ask the Derby woman if she understands why the woman in my story was so reluctant to use her tongue.

The woman from Derby nods. 'But did she, in the end? Did she give in and use her tongue?'

'She did. She did. And he gave her the money, and he left and she never spoke of what had happened, never told a living soul.'

'Gosh,' the woman from Derby says.

It is not a word you hear very often these days.

Gosh.

'What kind of despicable things?' is her next question.

Despicable is another word you don't hear very often.

The chances of somebody coming up to you in a courtroom, after the verdict has been handed down, and saying, 'Gosh, you are despicable,' must be extremely remote indeed.

I tell her about his despicable acts in considerable detail, and she pretends to be shocked, but it brings colour to her cheeks and there's a coy look to her as she murmurs, 'Still, thirty five thousand pounds.'

I smile, and pat my jacket pocket, and her brow furrows, and I raise an eyebrow, and there's a sudden sparkle in her eyes and for a long, long moment she believes that I have thirty five thousand pounds for her.

She whispers, 'You're not ugly at all,' and she's right, because as we have already established, for the purposes of this story, I am gorgeous. But then I laugh and tell her that I'm a writer and the story of the lottery winner with the cash for sex offer is from one of my short stories. She looks disappointed. I say, forget the money, I'm still capable of despicable acts. And that gets her laughing, where really, it shouldn't. She asks me if that's really how the story ends and I tell her no, that after the lottery winner left the woman went back down to the bar and ordered a bottle of champagne, being thirty five thousand pounds better off, but when she tried to pay for it the bar man held her twenty up to the light and said it was counterfeit, and upon further examination, they all were. She took the thirty thousand pounds out of her bag and threw them on the ground and stamped and tore at them, and just at that point her boyfriend returned, all ready to apologise, but such was her rage that she blurted out what had happened, and he stormed out again, this time for good.

My woman goes, 'Oh!' and 'Oh!' and that's just a *horrible* story.

She's quite drunk now, and she is relatively easily persuaded to her room. She finds it exciting, at first, the tearing off of the clothes and the fumbling and tumbling, because her boyfriend might return at any moment, but when we make love she seems disappointed that I do not perform despicable deeds upon her, and she urges me to hurry up and finish, which is difficult now that I can sense her regret.

As I lay upon her, I say there was an alternative ending to that story about the lottery winner and the woman of easy but expensive virtue.

And she says, 'What?' as in what are you talking about the short story for while you're supposed to be finishing off.

And I say, she didn't really go down to the bar and find out she'd been fobbed off with dodgy banknotes. Didn't you pick up on the fact that if she worked in a bank, she would probably have recognised straight away that the twenties were fake?

She sighs and says: 'Well, *what* then?'

My lips move to her ear and I whisper, 'The reason she never spoke about it again was that she couldn't. When she put her tongue in his mouth, he bit it off. She bled to death there beneath him, and he stared at her the whole time she was dying, and she couldn't move because of the weight of him upon her, and the fact that he was still inside her.'

I think it is unlikely that she will have an orgasm now.

'What kind of a writer are you anyway?' she hisses as she tries to get out from under me. 'Who would come up with a nasty, disgusting sort of a story like that?'

And I tell her that when I was learning how to become a writer, the best piece of advice my tutor ever gave me was to write about what you know.

He was a good creative writing teacher.

He came to our prison every week.

But he always had a problem with my unhappy endings.

NIPD BLUE

They're in the car, outside a video shop on the Antrim Road. *Planet of the Tapes.*

His has nothing to do with the video shop. Or the Antrim Road. It has to do with John Cooley standing there with his sunglasses and his confident smile and looking about him like he owns the world. They're going to take him down a peg or two.

Maybe even three, if they feel like it.

Software. John Cooley's about to join the modern world.

It's an unmarked car, but they're in uniform. There's no mistaking them, really, but Cooley doesn't budge, not even when they're right up in his face. He has a scar at the base of his scalp; when he raises an eyebrow, just one, the scar arches up like it's pointing at his brain. He's saying: I'm too fancy for you boys with your fancy new uniforms and your fruity little hats. You're still RUC, you're still SS-RUC. A ceasefire and a make-over isn't going to change that.

'John-Boy, how are ye?' says Walsh.

'Fine and dandy,' says Cooley.

'Would ye mind comin' down to the station with us?' says Philpott.

'Not at all,' says Cooley, smiles, and then pauses. He looks about him. Up to the sky. Back down and his eyes are all narrow and inquisitive. 'You don't think I've done something, do yees?'

They give him the supercilious smiles. 'Of course not, John-Boy,' says Walsh, 'we just want a wee chat. About life in general.'

'Life?' says Cooley.

'We hope so,' says Philpott, 'unless they bring back the death penalty first, you evil fucker. Now get in the back of the car.'

'Fuck off,' says Cooley.

'Fuck off yourself,' says Philpott, 'and get in the car while you're at it.'

'Are we gonna have to make you?' says Walsh.

'Fuckin' right you are.'

'C'mon, John-Boy,' says Philpott, 'don't make us call for back-up.'

'Up to you,' says Cooley, 'but my back up is bigger than your back-up.'

His back-up can cause rioting in north Belfast for weeks at a time. Or so he still likes to think. But the reality it, since the peace thing, since they gave up their guns, or at least buried them to use later, there isn't the same vandalistic malevolence; besides, since the Brits pulled out there aren't the same shops any more; all the nationals have sneaked off, leaving just the crappy little locals. No point in lootin' those, it's like lootin' yourself.

They stand looking at each other. Then Philpott taps him on the arm and says, 'We've a new interrogator down at the station.'

'Big fuckin' deal.'

'He's the best in the business.'

'Big fuckin' deal.'

'Isn't a hood he hasn't cracked yet.'

'Big fuckin' deal.'

'He could reduce you to putty.'

'Aye, right.'

The video shop is closing for the night. The shutters are coming down. The owner looks suspiciously at them, but he doesn't say anything. Cooley nods across. The owner looks a little bit scared, and a little bit hopeful that the cops will drag Cooley off.

'Chicken,' says Philpott.

'What?'

'Big chicken leg. John Cooley.'

'Who're you callin' a fuckin' chicken?'

'You, ar-buck-buck-buck-buck-buck.'

'He'd crack you in no time,' says Walsh.

'Like an egg, you fuckin' chicken bastard,' says Philpott.

'Fuck away off.'

'Chicken.'

'Chicken.'

'Chicken.'

'Chicken.'

'Right,' says John Cooley.

****

They put him in the interview room. They remove his cigarettes and deprive him of coffee. There is no air conditioning. It's hot. They leave him for an hour. He starts to sweat, but it's just the heat, he's not worried. Not John Cooley. They've tried every combination before: good cop-bad cop; good cop-good cop; bad cop-bad cop; lady cop-lady cop; ugly lady cop-ugly lady cop; good looking lady cop-ugly lady cop; fuckin' fantastic looking lady cop-fuckin' fantastic looking lady cop. They've tried violence, they've tried abuse, they've tried common sense and reasoning, they've tried bribery, they've tried to turn him into a squealer. Thus far, he hasn't given them a single fucking thing. But now there's software.

Philpott says to him, as he's setting the gear up, 'You ever used a computer, John?'

'What's the fuckin' point?' Cooley sneers.

Philpott shrugs. 'It's the new thing.'

'Big fuckin' deal.'

'What you do,' Walsh says, 'is just sit there, and the computer asks you some questions. Simple as that.'

'Where's my solicitor?' Cooley asks.

'You're not entitled to a solicitor, John-Boy,' says Walsh.

Cooley laughs. 'Course I fuckin' am. Go get him.'

Walsh laughs back. 'Sorry, old son, but you're not. You're only entitled to have a solicitor present if we're going to question you. And we're not going to question you.'

'Well what the fuck am I here for then?'

'*We're* not, *it* is.' Walsh points at the computer. 'Legally it's a bit of a grey area. Doubtless it will be sorted out in due course. But for the mean time, you're not entitled to a solicitor.'

Cooley glances at the squat grey box on the table. 'So I'll just fuckin' ignore it then.'

'Ah, no, you can't do that, John. You have to respond to the questions. You know that. You know the government removed the right to silence a long time ago, you have to answer. Make any old shit up you want, but you have to answer.'

Cooley looks doubtfully at the computer. 'And what if I destroy the fuckin' thing?'

'Then we have you for damaging police property.'

Cooley shrugs. 'Okay, fuck away off and leave me to it then.' They nod and turn to the door. Cooley calls them back. 'If you ask me,' he says, 'youse are all fuckin' bonkers.'

'We're not askin', John-Boy,' says Walsh.

****

There is perhaps three minutes of silence. Just Cooley's steady breathing. There's a camera in the light-fitting, so they can see it all on the screen upstairs. They're placing bets.

'He's mine,' says Walsh.

'Not a chance,' says Philpott.

'Fear of the new,' says Walsh.

'Philpott shrugs, and watches, and waits.

****

The voice is plummy-English. He had expected something electronic, like that cripple Hawking he'd seen on the box. But plummy English. The most annoyingly plummy Colonel Mustard in the Conservatory English.

It says, 'Did you murder Delores Watson?'

Cooley sits back. Like he's going to answer a fucking machine. And then he remembers what they said and he leans forward and hisses:

'Yeah, I cut her fucking head off.' He cackles.

A light flashes.

Cooley looks at the computer. Upstairs Philpott asks if the software can cope with sarcasm.

'Did you murder Delores Watson?'

'I answered that.'

'Did you murder Delores Watson?'

'I answered that.'

'Did you murder Delores Watson?'

'Oh fuck off.'

'Did you murder Delores Watson?'

'I told you to fuck off!'

'Did you murder Delores Watson?'

'Murdered her. Fucked her. Slit her throat.'

'Did you murder Delores Watson?'

'Yeah, I killed her.'

The light flashes again. Then nothing. Cooley leans closer, examining the machine. He looks to the door. He sits back. Folds his arms. Taps his foot. Reaches into his pocket for a fag, then remembers they took them off him. He pulls at his lip. He looks to the door. Finally he leans forward and says, 'No, I didn't.'

The light flashes.

'Did you kill Delores Watson?'

'No, I didn't.'

'Did you kill Delores Watson?'

'No, I didn't, okay?'

'Did you kill Delores Watson?'

'I hardly fucking know her.'

'Did you kill Delores Watson?'

'Fuck *off*.'

'Did you kill Delores Watson?'

'I'm tellin' you, I didn't know her.'

'Past tense now.'

'*What*?'

'Past tense now.'

'What the...?'

'Did you kill Delores Watson?'

'No, what did you mean by...?'

'Did you kill Delores Watson?'

'No!'

'Did you kill Delores Watson?'

'I'm tellin' you, I didn't touch...'

'Did you kill Delores Watson?'

'Will you shut the fuck up about Delores Watson?'

'Did you kill Delores Watson?'

'Fuck...'

'Did you kill Delores Watson?'

'Fuck off and...'

'Is your mother still alive?'

'What...?!'

'Did you kill Delores Watson?'

'Not that...not that! Why did you...?'

'Did you kill Delores Watson?'

'Why did you mention my mum?!'

'Did you kill Delores Watson?'

'Will you shut the fuck up about that stupid whore...what about my mum? What's this got to do with...?' He sits back, breathing hard. 'Where does my mum come into this? What the fuck has she...?' There is no response. He sits forward. He bites at a nail. He looks to the door. Back to the machine.

A green light flashes.

'What?' he says.

There is no response.

'I didn't kill her,' he says quietly. Still nothing. He sighs. He shakes his head. 'Look. This is stupid. We had a row, okay? I mean she was a stupid wee tart.' He waits. No question. No light. 'She took me back to her place, okay? All right? But then she didn't want to know. Real prick teaser, okay? We had a fight. I hardly touched the stupid cow.'

'Did you kill Delores Watson?'

'Christ! No! Okay! No!'

'Did you kill Delores Watson?'

'No! For fuck sake! She fell over and cracked her head, that's all, that's all. She said she was okay and I left, okay?'

'Did you kill Delores Watson?'

'I don't know!'

'What would your mother say?'

'What?! Jesus!'

'What is this obsession with...'

'Did you kill Delores Watson?'

'...my fucking mother?!'

'Did you kill Delores Watson?'

'I don't know! I don't know! What do you want me to say?'

'Did you kill Delores Watson?'

'I don't know! I didn't wait!'

'Tell mummy...'

'This isn't fucking funny!'

'Did you kill Delores Watson?'

'Yes! Okay! I killer her! She was askin' for it! She tried to rip me off! I thumped her! She fell down! She cracked her head! She didn't get up! There was blood everywhere and I fucking legged it, okay?! Satisfied? Just shut the fuck...'

'Did you kill Delores Watson?'

He slumps down on the table, shaking his head and says weakly: 'Yes, I killed Delores Watson.'

'Did you kill Delores Watson?'

'*Yes.*'

'On your mother's grave?'

'*Yes*. On my mother's grave.'

****

The door opens. Cooley is crying, head down.

'Relax, John-Boy,' says Walsh, crossing and switching off the machine.

'I didn't mean to,' Cooley says.

'Didn't mean to what?' says Philpott, lighting a fag for him.

'Kill Delores Watson.'

'You didn't kill anyone.'

'She's fine,' says Walsh, 'though she wants you done for assault.'

'We were just trying out the software,' says Walsh, 'nothing was recorded.'

'It's your word against her's,' says Philpott. 'You'll get off with a caution. Relax, John-Boy. You want a tissue?'

****

He is standing outside the video shop on the Antrim Road. *Planet of the Tapes*. This has nothing to do with the Antrim Road. Or the video shop. It has to do with John Cooley and his faded smile and the sunglasses he seems to hide behind.

They get out of their unmarked car. They approach from a different direction so that he doesn't see them. Walsh taps him on the shoulder.

Cooley lets out a yell, and spins.

'What the…?!' he says when he sees who it is. 'Ah…fuck yees…' He pulls out a cigarette. He looks at them and shakes his head. 'Fuckin' computers,' he says.

'Did you kill Delores Watson?' Walsh says, identical BBC plummy. He's laughing. 'Sucker,' he says. 'Can't believe you fucking fell for that, John-Boy. A fucking box with a couple of lights attached and me chattin' to you from upstairs. You fucking half wit.'

Cooley nods.

'You fucking idiot,' purrs Philpott. '*Software*'

'Hardware,' says Cooley, and pulls out his gun.

****

He is led into an interview room. He is pale. The table is bare. Walsh comes in with another officer and they sit opposite him. The tape recorder is switched on and the cops make their introductions. Then Walsh says, 'Did you murder NIPD Detective Mark Philpott?'

Colin Bateman

The Case of Mrs Geary's Leather Trousers.

THERE aren't many private eyes in Belfast, and now, apparently, there's one less. I know this because his shop was right next to mine. His name was Malcolm Carlyle and he seemed a decent sort; he would call in for a chat and a browse now and again when business was slow. His business, that is. His business was called Private Eye, big yellow letters on a black background. Then one day he didn't open up, and I never saw him again, and that was the start of my problems because he was still listed in the Yellow Pages, but when people couldn't get a response on the phone well, they thought, he must be good, he's so busy, he's changed his number, gone ex-directory, so they'd come down to plead their case, find the door locked, stand back and take a look at the place and see my shop next door and think there must be some kind of a connection because you don't have a shop called Private Eye and a shop called No Alibis sitting side by side for no reason at all. So they'd come in and furtively browse through the crime books, all the time eying me up behind the counter, trying to work out if I could possibly be the private eye they were looking for and if there was a connecting door between the shops, and whether I did this bookselling thing as a kind of respectable cover for my night time manoeuvres on the cold, dark streets of Belfast. They'd gotten it wrong of course. Book selling is more cut throat than you can possibly imagine.

The first fella who actually approached me was called Robert Geary; he was a civil servant in the Department of Education in Bangor, he was married, he had three children aged from nine to twelve and he supported Manchester United. He told me all this while making a meal out of paying for an Agatha Christie novel, so I knew something was up. No-one had bought a Christie in years.

He said, 'My wife wears leather trousers.'

This, I thought, was starting to enter the realm of too much information.

'She's forty-two,' he said, and I raised a concerned eyebrow. 'I know, I keep telling her she's too old for them, but she doesn't listen. The problem is she asked me to get them cleaned at our usual place, it's the only dry cleaners she trusts, except I was late for work and so I took them to this other place, do you know it – it's called Pressed for Time on the Castlereagh Road? – but they lost them and they were very nice about it and paid me what they cost, except my wife threw a fit anyway and called me all the names of the day and then a couple of weeks ago I was out shopping and I saw the exact same trousers walking down Royal Avenue, except no sooner had I seen them than I lost them in the crowds , so I went back to the dry cleaners and said I'd seen them walking down Royal Avenue but they said there was nothing they could do, so I didn't want to phone the police because they'd tell me to take a run and jump and so I phoned Malcolm Carlyle, Private Eye, and he said he'd see what he could do, but then when I didn't hear back from him and he didn't answer his phone, I thought I'd come down and see him. Except he's not there.'

'No he's not,' I said.

'And now I have to get them back, because as sure as hell the wife's going to be out shopping one day and she'll see them and then there'll be blood on the streets, and some of its going to be hers, and some of its going to be the other woman's, and some of it's going to be mine and I can do without that. I'm five years from retirement. We retire early in the Civil Service. We're going to buy a place in Cyprus.'

'Why don't you just get her some new ones?' I asked.

'Because these were a designer pair, I bought them in America, in Texas, near the Alamo, it's my favourite film, there's not another pair like them in Ireland, and possibly continental Europe.'

'I see,' I said, and charged him £4.50 for the Christie.

****

He left me his number in case the private eye turned up again, and I said it seemed unlikely, but he said keep it anyway, and if there's anything you can do I'd very much appreciate it, and then he hurried out because there was another customer who'd come in and now wanted served, so I didn't get the chance to ask what he meant by *if there's anything you can do*. The next customer was just looking for directions. He wanted to know where Queens University was. I said I wasn't sure and sold him a street map. It was only around the corner, but the profit was the difference between burger and steak.

Over the next couple of days I was up to my neck in stock taking and didn't give the leather trousers another thought, but then I finally got back behind the till and found the note I'd made of his number and seeing as how I'd an average of forty-three minutes to kill between customers I started thinking about the possibilities, and that's how I came to phone Pressed for Time to enquire about the mysterious disappearance and even more mysterious re-appearance of Mrs Geary's leather trousers.

'And you are, who?' the man at the other end said with enough suspicion for me to say the first name that came to mind, other than my own, for I had a business and its reputation to protect, 'Lawrence Block.'

'Like the crime writer,' said the man, unexpectedly.

'Like the crime writer,' I said. 'Except I'm definitely not in the book business.'

'What business would you be in then? You know, I can't go giving out confidential information to just anyone who phones up asking.'

I said, 'I'm representing Mr Geary and Mrs Geary in the matter of their leather trousers, and by the by, what kind of confidential information would a dry cleaners have to be worried about giving out anyway?'

'Oh you'd be surprised,' he said. 'We do police uniforms and prison officers uniforms and...' And then he caught himself on and said, 'But that's confidential. I'll, ah, get the manager.'

The manager came on and said gruffly, 'I've had it up to my back teeth with these leather trousers. Even though we don't accept responsibility for lost or damaged items we paid for them. I don't see what his problem is.'

'Well they had sentimental value,' I said.

'Sentimental leather trousers?' said the manager, then he sighed and his tone lightened a little and he said, 'It takes all sorts. Mr Block, is it?'

'Call me Larry.'

'What are you, a solicitor?'

I cleared my throat in a positive manner and said, 'If you don't accept any responsibility for lost or damaged items, why did you pay Mr Geary for the missing trousers.'

'Well the fact of the matter is we *didn't* pay Mr Geary, at least, not directly. We send our leather items out for specialist cleaning. *They* said they were damaged in the cleaning process, and *they* instructed us to pay Mr Geary and promised to reimburse us. Although I'm still waiting.'

'Well if they said they were damaged, how come those very same leather trousers were last seen hurrying down Royal Avenue at a great rate of knots?'

'Well I don't know. You'd have to take it up with them.'

So he gave me their number and said they were on the Newtownards Road and I thanked him for his time and I was about to phone them when the shop door opened and a tourist came in and asked if I could recommend the new John Grisham and I said, yes, if you're a moron.

****

Well it turns out John Grisham was on a signing tour of the UK, and not wanting to cause pandemonium wherever he went he was just calling at bookshops unannounced, which struck me as an inefficient way to do things, but each onto their own. Still I managed to pass it off as a joke because his face is right there on the back of his books, so I get to look at him at least six times a day, and of course I recognised you straight off I said, although in truth, shorn of good lighting and make-up he looked a lot heavier and his hair was longer and unkempt and his skin was blotchy and he seemed to have some kind of a rash on his neck. It's lucky that I myself was born with an honest kind of a face, as he seemed to accept that my off the cuff remark was a typical example of our much heralded troubles humour, etc. etc...

I made him a cup of coffee while he signed copies of his books, and seeing as how he was an American and not wishing to seem overawed by his wealth and celebrity, I related to him the story of Mrs Geary's leather trousers, putting extra emphasis on the fact that they'd originated in Texas, which is somewhere in the general region of where I believe he hails from originally, but he didn't seem very interested and kept trying to steer the conversation back to exactly how many copies of his next novel I planned to order, which wasn't a subject I was keen to explore. When he finished signing his books, he moved on to signing copies of books by other authors, which I thought was a little strange, but there didn't seem any harm in it, in fact, it was quite novel and I thought it might help me to move a lot of dead stock. There probably wouldn't be a huge profit in it, but it could mean the difference between eight slices of cooked ham in a re-sealable packet and a fresh gammon steak. But after he had gone and I was beginning to put the signed books out on display I realized that he had signed most of his books 'Johnny Grisham' and some of them 'David Grisham' and several 'The Lord God of All Hosts' and one 'How much does your piano weigh?', and I began to reflect on the capacity of the Irish to fall for anyone with an American accent, be they pauper, paranoid or president, and whatever gibberish they might care to spout.

I was not, therefore, in the best of moods when I finally came to phone Stick to Me, the leather goods cleaners, shortly before closing time. I made a point of not identifying myself this time, saying merely that I was phoning on behalf of a client, a Mr Geary, but before I could get on to the substance of my complaint the man at the other end said, 'Is that Mr Block?'

I cleared my throat in a positive manner and demanded to know what had happened to the leather trousers.

'They got torn up by the machinery. They were damaged beyond repair.'

'And yet they were spotted galloping down Royal Avenue.'

'We heard that. We can only presume that somebody rescued them from the skip behind our shop and stitched them back together.'

I immediately pounced on that. 'I thought they were damaged *beyond* repair.'

'Beyond the standard of repair we pride ourselves on. How close was your witness to them? They probably looked like a dog's dinner. Mr Block, Larry, the trousers are gone, we paid up, we paid up above and beyond, I think you should drop this – while you still can.'

It sat in the air for several long moments.

Then I cut the line. I put the receiver down and stood there, quite shocked by this unexpected turn of events. *While you still can.* I was being warned off. Threatened, even. It wasn't even a veiled threat. It was explicit, if understated, like a grenade in a cemetery.

The phone rang and I thanked God for the distraction. I said, 'Hello, No Alibis.'

And the same voice said, 'Is that Larry?'

My voice rose a couple of octaves as I gave him an innocent, 'Larry?'

And he said, 'Larry Block. I was speaking to him a minute ago and I got cut off and I hit caller ID and then I called the number and you answered the phone.'

'Well, I'm sorry, there's no Larry here.'

'What's the name of that place again?'

'What place?'

'You answered the phone and said hello no something.'

'Ah. No. You misheard. I said hello, Noah. Noah Alibees. That's my name. It's French Canadian originally. I design hats. Are you calling about a hat?'

It seemed to do the trick. He quickly apologised and rang off. When I put the phone down I found that my hands were damp, my shirt was sticking to my skin and my heart was beating ninety to the dozen.

****

Two days a week I employee a student called Jeff to mind the shop while I sit in the back office trying to make my books balance. He's young and keen and writes poetry and belongs to Amnesty International, but he'll grow out of all of these things. My office is close enough to the till so that I can hear what's going on in the store, in particular if Jeff is misusing the phone to call either his girlfriend or some Government agency to demand that a political prisoner be repatriated to Sierra Leone. In light of the previous day's threat I had considered not allowing Jeff to answer the phone at all, but a cursory examination of the books told me I wasn't in any position to turn away potential business, so by way of compromise I instructed Jeff to answer any incoming calls with a French accent, which he managed passably well, and to be as vague as possible until he was able to ascertain the nature of the enquiry. Vagueness for Jeff, truth be told, wasn't going to be a huge stretch.

I made him repeat *Noah Alibees* over and over until he got it just right. Then I said that if anyone called and asked for Larry he was to reply, 'There is no Larry here, would you like to buy a hat.' Towards noon I was just beginning to think that I might have gotten hold of the wrong end of the stick. There had been four phone calls, all of them either from customers or publishers reps. But then the fifth call came in and my carefully constructed cover story quickly began to unravel. I heard Jeff say, 'Noah Alibees, would you like to buy a hat,' and then, 'Yes, hats, all different types.' And then. 'No there's nobody called Larry Block here.' I moved from my desk in the back to the body of the shop. 'Nope, no Lawrence Block either.' Then with a piece of inspired improvisation Jeff added. 'You'd have to go to a mystery book shop to find Lawrence Block.' Jeff saw me; he smiled and gave me the thumbs up. Then he said, 'No trouble at all,' and hung up. When I approached the till he said, 'You look a little pale, what's the matter?'

I put my hands on the counter to steady myself, took a deep breath and said, 'I'm being intimidated by the owner of a shop which specializes in the cleaning and repair of leather goods.'

Jeff gave this due consideration. Then he said, 'Somebody's scrawled all over the John Grisham books.'

****

By the next day, and still being alive, and the shop not having been burned to the ground, I decided that I'd misinterpreted what the leather care man had to say, that his threat had been more about consulting his lawyers than tanning my hide. However, I didn't wish to push my luck by calling him again to confirm this or to ask further questions about Mrs Geary's trousers, so instead I turned to the internet. I keep a database of loyal customers and send them an e-newsletter once a month. It's all about building a relationship. I try to sell them the latest releases and they burden me with their personal problems. It's tiresome but necessary. On this occasion, however, I wasn't selling anything, I merely asked those of my lovely customers living in the greater Belfast area to keep an eye out for a pair of leather trousers, and described their design in considerable detail. I included the words 'substantial reward' without specifying that it was a £10 book token plus a signed copy of *Harry Potter and the Prisoner of Azkaban*, albeit signed by Jehovah's Vengeance Grisham.

I didn't hear anything for another three days, but then, slowly, reports began to come in, and then what had been a trickle became a fast flowing stream. The trousers were spotted again in Royal Avenue, at a cinema on the Belfast Road, at a concert in the Waterfront Hall featuring three black men who had once known someone who was in The Drifters, and twice again in Royal Avenue. It seemed like Royal Avenue was the place to be. Each of my informants who saw her there had observed the trousers between 12.30 and 1.30 pm, and reported their occupant as, and I quote, 'a big girl' wearing too much make-up and a short white beauticians' smock over the trousers. Putting two and two together, I decided to visit Boots the Chemist. As it happened I had a prescription that needed filled, so I was able to kill two birds with one stone. While standing in the pharmacy queue I kept a close eye on the make-up counters, and before very long I was rewarded with my first sight of Mrs Geary's leather trousers, which sent a shiver of anticipation, if not excitement, down my spine. I watched them for several minutes, moving up and down on the customer side of the counter as the large woman who inhabited them applied make-up to a pale woman in a pink woollen trouser suit; she was saying, 'Oh yes, that shade really suits you, and I'd tell you if it made you look like an old slut.'

The pharmacist then asked if I'd taken this particular type of anti-depressant before, and I said yes, twice daily for the past fifteen years. He asked if it worked for me and I said it was early days yet. I paid for the prescription, and it now being 12.30 I was pleased to see the woman in Mrs Geary's leather trousers finish with her client and hand over her cash desk key to a colleague. She then pulled on a short coat over her beautician's jacket and left the shop.

I hurried up to the beauty counter and said, 'Damn, I missed her...' The girl behind the counter looked unconcerned, but asked if she could help. 'Your colleague – in the leather trousers, she was checking out the availability of a certain perfume for me...but now I've missed her.'

'She'll be back at two.'

'Damn I have to get back to work - but I could phone to see how she got on – who should I ask for?'

'Ask for Natasha.'

'Natasha...?'

'Yes, Natasha.'

'Her surname...?'

'Just ask for Natasha. Natasha on the make-up counter.'

'But in case there's any confusion, her full name is...?'

'There's nobody else called Natasha.'

Mrs Geary's leather trousers were coming back at two, so there was no immediate panic.

'To tell you the truth,' I said to Laura, which is what it said on Laura's badge, 'she's not really helping me at all. I've been in three times and she keeps fobbing me off with excuses. So I'm really here to make a complaint. Can I speak to your supervisor?'

Laura looked surprised, but she nodded and went to the phone. A couple of minutes later a woman in a smart business suit approached me and said, 'I understand you wish to complain about Miss Irvine.'

****

Natasha Irvine returned from lunch forty minutes later. I was in position just to the left of the Boots front doors. She was a moon faced girl with big eyes. There were flakes of sausage roll pasty in the corners of her mouth and she gave a little jump when I said, 'Hello Natasha.'

She stopped and began to smile but then she realised she didn't know me, and she might have blushed, but it was difficult to tell with all the make up, which looked like the Max Factor equivalent of stone cladding.

'It is, Natasha Irvine, isn't it?' Her mouth dropped open a little. 'I wanted to talk to you about your leather trousers.'

I gave her my hard look, which is like my normal look, but harder. At this point, if she'd had any sense, she should have asked for ID, and I could have shown her my Xtravision card and my Kidney Donor Card and then rattled my prescription at her and dribbled off into the distance ranting about this or that, but as it happened my hard look proved more than adequate.

'Oh Christ,' she said, 'they're stolen, aren't they?'

I raised an eyebrow.

'Jesus wept,' she said, 'I took one look at them and I knew he couldn't afford them. My family owns this leather repair place on the Newtownards Road, so I know what costs what. But he swore to God he saved up. Christ.' She blew some air out of her cheeks and said, 'To tell you the God's honest truth, I don't even like them, I've piled the beef on since I had the twins, and they're cuttin' the hole off me. I only wear them to keep him happy. What am I going to do now?'

I gave her another long look. A thick sweat had broken out on her brow, and I decided to move quickly in case it set off an avalanche of make-up. 'Here's what we're going to do,' I said, and this time I did take out my wallet. 'I can't be bothered with pursuing this to court, the paperwork's a bloody nightmare. As it happens the owner's offered a reward. You tell your man they got stolen from your locker at work, he buys you another present, plus you're two hundred pounds better off.' I took out the money and held it out to her. 'Owner gets the trousers back, I don't have to do any pen pushing, you're in the money. How does that sound?'

'Too good to be true,' she said.

'It's a once in a life time offer,' I said.
She thought about that for just a few moments, then nodded quickly.
'But could you make it two-fifty?' she asked.

I shook my head. 'It's not your call, darlin',' I said, then held firm at two hundred and forty five.

****

When I got back to the shop I told Jeff to take the hats out of the window, then gave him the rest of the day off. I also gave him a nice bonus. 'What's this for?' he asked. 'Danger money,' I replied. I was feeling generous.

When he'd left I sat by the till, rested my feet on the counter, unwrapped a celebratory Twix and then called Mr Geary between the destruction of one stick and the devouring of the second. 'Guess who?' I virtually sang.

He made five unsuccessful guesses, so I told him, and he still seemed a little confused, so I reminded him, and then he said, 'Ah, right.' I didn't plunge straight in with the good news, I wanted him to know how much work I'd put in. So I described how I'd established the crime line from the moment he'd left his wife's leather trousers into Pressed for Time: how they'd sub-contracted them to the shop on the Newtownards Road, how the owner must have commented on their unique qualities to Miss Irvine's boyfriend who'd decided that they'd make a perfect gift. He'd then persuaded the owner to fabricate the story about them being damaged and then the owner had panicked when I'd applied just the right amount of pressure. Despite being in mortal fear for my life, I'd nevertheless managed to track down the trousers and make them secure. 'I have them back, Mr Geary,' I said, raising and admiring the chocolate covered biscuit, 'I have your wife's leather trousers.'

He seemed rather under whelmed. 'Oh – well, that's…ah, that's nice.'

'It cost me five hundred pounds, but I suppose it's a pretty cheap way to save a marriage.' He cleared his throat. I said, 'So do you want to come and pick them up?'

'Well, no,' he said.

'No?'

'Well the fact is, it turns out she never liked the trousers in the first place.'

'But…'

'She threw a wobbler out of my stupidity for losing them, not because of the trousers. I misunderstood.'

'But…they're beautiful trousers…'

'I know that, but apparently they cut the hole off her.'

'But I've spent…'

'Well that's your problem, I'm afraid.'

'But…but what am I supposed to do with…'

'Well perhaps you could give them to your own wife.'

The Twix was now melting in my hand.

'Yeah, I wish,' I sighed.

****

So I was two hundred and forty five pounds out of pocket on the trousers, not to mention the sleepless night, the rocketing of my blood pressure or the sixty five quid I'd spent on cheap hats from Dunnes. One day I'd meet the man who'd come up with the phrase, if you want to get ahead, get a hat, and I'd have a strong word or two. But in the meantime I'd a business to run. Besides, I have found that when all else fails, you can always fall back on fine writing to see you through a dark patch. The very next day an aspiring book collector came in enquiring about signed first editions, and I showed him one of the Grishams. He turned it over in his hand like he knew what he was doing and said, 'How much?'

'If you have to ask...' I said with as much disinterest as I could muster.

'No, really,' he said.

I made a quick calculation. Two forty five, plus sixty five for the hats, two hundred for my time and another fifty for being an unscrupulous cad. Five hundred and sixty, I said, and I could tell by the way he blanched that it was way over what he had in mind. But I have learned over all my years in business, that if you price something high enough, some sucker will eventually come along and fall for it. And so he pulled out his credit card and bought the Grisham and I was finally back in profit and also, I suppose, a wiser, more cautious man to boot.

I put the book in a nice bag for him and said if he was interested

I could maybe lay my hands on another one or two. He smiled nervously and quickly changed the subject.

'I really like your trousers,' he said.

I glanced lovingly down at them and nodded. 'Thanks,' I said, 'they are nice, but they really do cut the hole off you.'

The Prize

I have been asked to write this piece for The Guardian. Although it is a paper that many of my artist friends swear by, I do not purchase it myself. Nevertheless I have agreed to write this piece seeing as how all of my fellow nominated artists have agreed to do so.

I think a work of art must stand by itself and be judged. All I really need to say about my work is that I paint landscapes, big ones, often covering an entire wall. If you have four walls I will cover them in one continuous landscape so that if you stand in the middle of the room and rotate 360 degrees it should be just like standing in a real field. It is more complicated if you have five walls. In the past I have been asked if I paint landscapes as a reaction to the time I spent locked in a cell in prison. I do not know. It is not the sort of thing you say to yourself, 'I am painting this as a reaction to the time I spent locked in a cell in prison.' You say, 'I am painting this because it is pretty.'

Some of my friends say, 'Why not just take a photograph?' They do not understand art.

My first exhibition was held in a small gallery at the rear of a turf accountants just off the Falls Road. It had not previously operated as a gallery but as a storage room full of betting slips and paperwork relating to the business. I asked the owner if he would mind if I threw out all of his records in order to open the gallery, and he did not protest. So I opened the first art gallery in West Belfast, which apart from the paintings is one of my greatest achievements. We have not yet built a separate entrance to the gallery, so you have to come in through the turf accountant's. Some of the clientele in the turf accounts ask if I ever paint horses. I say perhaps, one day. The problem is that horses do not stay still. I understand that they can sleep standing up, but one cannot rely on the muse striking at exactly the same time as the horse falls asleep. And it is best not to drug them. I may however put some very small horses into my landscapes. They would not actually be small, but normal sized horses. But they would look small against the landscape.

I thought a good name for the gallery would be 'Easel', which is a term familiar to painting fans and other artists.

Sometimes I am amazed at how far I have come in such a short time. It is only two years since that first exhibition at 'Easel'. I displayed fourteen of my best landscapes and invited my family, friends and members of Belfast's artistic fraternity. Every single one was sold, even though no pressure was put on anyone to buy. However, the art critic from the *Belfast Evening News* arrived, and drank the wine, but did not put anything in his newspaper. When I later phoned him to complain, he very quickly agreed to write a review. By this time unfortunately the paintings had been sold and dispersed to my cousin's house. I suggested to the art critic that he either come to my cousin's house – it's a big house which he bought with the compensation he received as a result of an unfortunate joy-riding accident – or re-write the review from memory. The art critic from the *Belfast Evening News* chose to write it from memory. This was understandable, because he said in his review that once seen, my landscapes could never be forgotten.

The *Irish Reporter* also published a review and commented favourably on the 'bold use of metaphor' in my landscapes, but suggested the addition of animals to help add perspective. I immediately visited the reviewer at his home, and he observed that I'd put on a bit of weight since the hunger strike. We had a long discussion about art. And then

I asked him for a list of animals which might find favour with critics like himself. He thought it was a bad idea to try and please critics in this way, but I said, 'You're never too old to learn.' So even though it was past three o'clock in the morning and I was sitting on the end of his bed, he agreed to discuss further the possible animals I might include. He favoured the more traditional approach, i.e. pigs, or cows, or sheep, or possibly a goat. I am more cutting edge, and suggested a giraffe or a water buffalo. It would make people look twice to see a view of the Antrim Hills with a giraffe in it. They would say, 'What is that giraffe doing there in the Antrim Hills?' and wonder if it had escaped from the zoo.

Great art makes you think.

I was disappointed to later discover that this man was only a part time art critic, and normally reported on farming matters for the *Irish Reporter*, which explains his preference for less exotic animals in my landscapes.

The only newspaper to give a fairly negative review of my first exhibition at 'Easel' was the *East Belfast Spectator*, which I feel had more to do with the fact that it is from the wrong side of the tracks to me, and showed its ignorance of the healing powers of art by focussing not on the paintings, but on the painter. They raked up all kinds of inconsequential detail about my past life and did not once mention the quality of the paintings or my use of metaphor.

Critical acceptance is of course essential to an emerging artist, whether it be a writer or a poet, a sculptor or a painter of landscapes like myself. The funny is that most people who partake in the arts are quite shy and self conscious, and find it difficult to cultivate the relationships with people in positions of influence which are necessary to ignite a fledgling career. Perhaps because I might be considered a late starter, and have been forced to develop close inter-personal skills in a small paramilitary unit, I have not found this difficult and have gone out of my way to meet critics, gallery owners and subsidy providers, often outside of their intimidating office environments - perhaps in a car park, or as they leave their homes early in the morning. I have found that a quiet word of explanation makes all the difference when it comes to a good review, securing an exhibition or provision of a cash grant. Art is a complicated business and the meaning of certain works is not always apparent, even to the most professional and diligent observer. For example, my landscape, *Fields With Trees and Bushes, Outside Lisburn*, even though it features a wildebeest – they have one stuffed in the Belfast Museum, which got me round the problem of having to keep it still – is nevertheless to all intents and purposes merely a landscape. However, I was able to call at the holiday home of the radio producer who had approved a negative review and point out that although the painting only showed hills, trees, bushes and a wildebeest outside Lisburn, beyond the hills, out of sight, is the Long Kesh prison camp where I was sentenced to thirty seven years for murder, and he agreed that this completely altered his views of the painting in question.

Since those early days my artistic career has been something of a rollercoaster and I feel truly blessed that wherever I have gone, whatever challenges I have undertaken, I have been welcomed with open arms by Northern Ireland's artistic community. In fact, those arms have been opened so widely that not only has room been made for me, but also for my whole slowly developing school of artistic endeavour, which has been allowed to assume a position of influence, or indeed control, over the whole artistic community. Not only has exhibition space, generous sponsorship and impressive grants been made available to me, but also to Thomas 'Biro' McIntyre, POW Long Kesh, 82-87; Malachy 'Three Strokes' Mahood, POW Long Kesh, 85-92; and Edna O'Boyle, Armagh POW, 86-95, who famously began her career in textiles by crocheting a bullet proof vest. In addition, Christopher 'Concrete' Corcoran is now Artist in Residence at the Castle Court Shopping Centre, while Patrick 'Three Shovels' O'Hare was appointed to the Police Board's Mural Evaluation and Preservation Committee only last year, despite the fact that he's been on the run since 1986.

When the shortlist for this year's prize was announced I realized that I would have to answer many questions about my past. What I say is that the past is a different country. Like Algeria. I also use the example of *The Godfather Trilogy* where Michael Corleone is always trying to take the family legit. When I said this, a Smart Alec journalist pointed out that each *Godfather* movie ended in a bloody massacre and I had to say, 'It's only a bloody movie.'

I would like to say that my favourite holiday destination is America as they have fantastic landscapes into which I could easily insert some of our own exotic animals, such as an Irish Wolf Hound, or a Jack Russell to get the locals thinking about art. Except – I'm not allowed into that country because of my past history.

The nominations for this year's Learner's Prize puts the seal on what has been an astonishing few years for myself personally and the development in general of the arts in Northern Ireland. I firmly believe that this competition is not about winning, but, as we have shown with the Northern Ireland peace agreement, about taking part. There is no room in the arts for triumphalism, for we are all but roaming wildebeest ourselves in a larger landscape. Merely because you do not understand a work of art – for example, an unmade bed, or a sheep in formaldehyde – it doesn't mean that it is without merit at all. Everyone has to start somewhere. And after all, who would have thought that coming from my background that I would emerge, as the judges have assured me on each of the visits I have paid to their places of residence, as the favourite to take home this year's Learner's Prize?

NATIONAL ANTHEM

Produced by Ransom Productions.
Directed by Rachel O'Riordan
Anthem – Lyrics by Colin Bateman, Music by Conor Mitchell.

Cast – Miche Doherty, Stuart Graham, Alan McKee and Niamh Quinn.

The World Premiere was held at the Grand Opera House, Belfast, during the Ulster Bank Belfast Festival 2010.

A rehearsal room, featuring an array of costumes, props and musical instruments to be used in a celebration of Northern Irish history, arts and culture. At the rear there is something tall hidden under a sheet. There is a keyboard, amps, computer screen, full length mirror. The door opens and MILLER appears, stylishly dressed and carrying a brief case. He walks over to the keyboards as if to inspect them thoroughly, but only presses one note, listens, and decides that the set-up will suffice. He removes a coat hanger from his briefcase and slips his jacket over it. He looks around the room, trying to decide where to hang it. As he crosses the room he stops before the object hidden under a sheet. He briefly peeks under it, shakes his head and moves on to a rail of theatrical costumes and carefully makes space in the middle so that none of them are touching his coat. He turns from the rail, and catches sight of himself in the full length mirror. He examines his figure from several angles, nodding appreciatively. He is then distracted by footsteps on the stairs. He RACES across the room, slams the briefcase shut and slips in behind the keyboard, switching it on and instantly beginning to play something cocktail lounge jazzy.

The door opens and O'HARE enters, short of breath. His face is lost inside a giant parka, and there's a bag over his shoulder. O'Hare looks back down the stairs, and then closes the door and leans back against it, catching his breath and pulls the hood down.

O'HARE   Wow! Would you look at this place!

MILLER   Magic, isn't it?

O'Hare begins to pick through the items on display.

O'HARE   You here long?

MILLER   It's not a problem. Good trip?

O'HARE   Drove up, so I did. Galway. Arse feels like it's had a stroke. You?

MILLER   Straight from the airport.

O'Hare takes off the parka and carelessly throws it to one side.

O'HARE   Switzerland isn't it?

MILLER   Zurich.

O'HARE   Zurich. Right. You do the skiing? Haven't the knees for it anymore. You do the skiing?

MILLER   Insurance won't let me. *He holds up his hands.* The oul mitts.

O'HARE   Makes sense. *He mimes typing.* I should get my own insured, but they'd never pay out. If I lost my hands in a bizarre gardening accident they'd argue I could still type. Attach something to my stumps. Maybe I wouldn't have stumps. I suppose they could put those sticker things to my head and I could pick out the letters with...or my toes, you could train them up strong, couldn't you? Could you do that?

He begins to circle the object hidden under a sheet.

MILLER   What?

O'HARE   Play the piano with your feet.

MILLER   I...

O'HARE   So what's *this*?

MILLER   This thing we're doing tomorrow, the celebration, they had a public vote, a national animal for Northern Ireland. Like koala bears down under.

O'HARE   Right. Good. Brilliant. And this won?

MILLER   Yup.

O'HARE   May I?

MILLER   Be my guest.

O'Hare nods for several long moments, and then whips the sheet off. There is a giant 'stuffed' badger, as tall as a man, standing erect. O'Hare stares at it while Miller plays some stealthy badger music.

O'HARE   A *panda*?

MILLER   No, you Clampett. Badger!

O'HARE   Badger?! Right, right enough...badger? Fuckinhell. I suppose you can't argue with a public vote.

MILLER   Actually, you can. A giraffe came first, but it was disqualified. It's not native, apparently.

O'HARE   Badger!

MILLER   Snooky

O'HARE   You what?

MILLER His name is Snooky. Snooky the Badger. Like World Cup Willie, but not.

O'HARE *nooky?* Boysadear. So where'd the swan come in?

MILLER The swan? No idea. Would that be your choice?

O'HARE (*Pause, studying him, shrugging*) This is an odd one, isn't it? Talk about panic stations, a National Anthem to go along with all this malarkey and we want it *now*. Your name came up, I thought this'll be interesting.

MILLER They didn't tell me it was you until they picked me up at the airport. I got the impression the others said no. It's a poisoned chalice, isn't it? No-one's going to thank us for it. One side likes it, the other's going to hate it. That's why they've put us together. They think that'll fool them. It won't. Both sides will hate us.

O'HARE (*Pause*) They picked you up at the airport? They told me to bring receipts. *He crosses to a window and peers out, before checking that it is secure.* But bloody hell, they're cuttin it fine.

MILLER Only date I had free…

O'HARE Yeah…likewise, but still. We're not fuckin monkeys.

MILLER Monkeys?

O'HARE You know what I mean. *He mimes rapidly clashing cymbals together.* Although for this money, I'm prepared to monkey up. Eh? Me last fee was a bottle of wine and a snog with a half wit.

Miller starts playing again.

MILLER   They're not paying me. Expenses.

O'HARE   Whaddya mean they're not paying you? I hammered them for every last farthing. Get *into* them. Shower of fucking chancers!

MILLER   I volunteered.

O'HARE   You volunteered what, to not get paid? If there's a government, a department, a committee, they have the money, it's your job to squeeze it out of them. Bottom line, always get paid. Always get paid. We're the real deal. We've done stuff. Get fucking paid. Who do they think they are?

MILLER   I was offered, but I turned it down.

O'HARE   Why the fuck would you turn it down?

MILLER   I suppose...giving something back.

O'HARE   Giving something back.

MILLER   Giving something back.

O'HARE   (*Cackles*) We could take that to the court of dubious decisions!. It would imply, surely, having been given something in the first place.

MILLER   I believe we were. It's like pass the parcel.

O'HARE   Aye, and it's a fucken letter bomb! *He mimics a bomb exploding, then examines his hands*. Could you play the piano with hooks? I think I could get by with one hook, but two? That's a serious masturbation injury. We should get this party started. How do you like to work?

MILLER   Quickly.

O'HARE   Really? I'm a bit of a slow burn myself.

MILLER   I'm on the seven o'clock flight to London tonight, and then on to Vienna.

O'HARE   Christ. hey didn't tell me that. I was going to stretch it out to dinner and a couple of bottles of wine, oil the oul cogs, know what I mean? (PAUSE) Vienna's not in Switzerland. You probably know that.

MILLER   I'm starting a world tour. Twenty six countries.

O'HARE   Twenty six countries! But I expect it's not as glamorous as it sounds. There'll be a lot of those little shitty ones like Belarus and Azkaban. You're not giving very much back if you're only staying till seven! We're professionals, and if we have to we can turn it on like a tap, but sometimes something gets stuck in the pipes, nobody's fault, just gets stuck and it won't come, it won't fucking come, what'll we do then, what if we manage nothing and they don't pay us? Me. Don't pay me. You really think we can do this by seven?

MILLER   Five.

O'HARE   Five! Do it by five?

MILLER   Flight's at seven, I'll need to leave here by five.

O'HARE   Fucking hell. That's not long. That's not long.

MILLER   It's not long, but they need it quick.

O'HARE   Aye, aye, you're right. You're right. So what's it to be? You don't want some fucking dirge like God Save the Queen, so we don't, and you don't want some fucking South American effort that sounds like an orchestra tuning up, you want something you can put your hand on your heart and really thump out. Like the French one. *He hums part of La Marseillaise* The American one's not bad, not bad but wanky. Do you know what I mean? You want hand on the heart, but you don't want wanky. You want pride, but not ego, we want to punch the air, but not so much that other people want to rip your head off. You want it to inspire, you want if it was played in a movie, you'd know the cavalry were about to come over the hill and save you. The Germans (*he hums it*), they're really fucked, every time you hear that you're heading for the bomb shelters.

MILLER   Simple is good.

O'HARE   Simple is great. Let's face it, apart from tomorra, it'll be school kids and rugger buggers who'll be singing it. You want it simple, repetitive.

Miller begins to bash out a simple, repetitive tune on the piano. O'Hare listens. Miller finishes. O'Hare nods along.

O'HARE   Not that simple. We want deceptively simple. Or should that be deceptively complex. Right fuck. Listen to this. *Consulting paper* So long as there is the earth and the heavens. So long as the world endures. So long as there is life in the world...

MILLER   You wrote...?

O'HARE   So long as a single Afghan breathes, there will be this

Afghanistan! (BEAT) No, I'm just saying. That's the sort of crap...no offence Afghanistan! That famously unified nation. This is mine: I love you forever, your skies, your air sets my heart in tune as if it were a flute. In Spring, Oh mother mine, the fragrance from your mango-groves...

MILLER   Oh for fuck sake...

O'HARE   Bangladesh! But...DO YOU SEE WHAT I MEAN? We have to be so down the fucken middle...I mean, I mean, I mean, I mean...Tayto Cheese and Onion Crisps! We should mention Tayto Castle.

MILLER   You cannot mention Tayto Castle in the National Anthem.

O'HARE   Why not?!

MILLER   Because it's bloody mental.

O'HARE   Crisps. It's the one thing that unites us all. Everyone likes Tayto cheese and onion.

MILLER   There would be copyright issues, product placement...

O'HARE   So what? You want the Glens of Antrim and the Giant's Causeway? They're just product placement too.

MILLER   God's product placement. It's a different...

O'HARE   Do you remember that bridge, the rope bridge, the Carrick-a-rede rope bridge?

MILLER   Aye...*clicking fingers*...up at...

O'HARE   Aye, Carrick-a-Rede. Holy fuck! It was like that bridge in Indiana Jones, but like with an Atlantic gale swinging it, and the drop, Jesus, the drop, to the rocks and the sea and the...my dad made us go across it, the twelve O'Hare's brickin it, not only that, once you got across, you had to go back. I got stuck in the middle, just me on me ownio, and he wouldn't come back for me, and he wouldn't let any of the others and he was screaming at me, get off the fucking bridge, get off the fucking bridge!

MILLER   So what happened?

O'HARE   I got off the fuckin bridge.

MILLER   There's twelve of you?

O'HARE   Twelve O'Hare's, aye. Well, eight. I polish it a bit for the Yanks.

MILLER   Eight kids?

O'HARE   Not eight, no, six. My line, you have to do an Angela's Ashes thing or you're fucked. Or not fucked as the case may...

MILLER   You're seeing them while you're back?

O'HARE   Yeah. Maybe. Probably not. Six in a bed we were, that's a fact. But we were never close. My dad...*my dad*, his idea of bonding, his idea of something we could all do together, out into the back garden, he gives the order and we clod the Proddies with bricks, up and over the wall. Like Hitler's V2 Rockets, destination non specific.

He pretends to lob something through the air. Miller looks at him soberly.

MILLER Where was this? Wasn't anywhere near Argyle Street?

O'HARE Argyle? Aye, that's where I...

MILLER When would this a been?

O'HARE Christ, I don't know. The roarin' Seventies.

MILLER My brother, my brother Alan was blinded by a brick, came over the wall at Argyle, July 11th, 1974.

O'HARE Get away to fuck. Really?

MILLER Really.

O'HARE Really?

MILLER Really.

O'HARE Isn't that a quare coincidence? I used to throw bricks, and he got bricked.

MILLER Isn't it just.

O'HARE What the fuck are you looking at? It wasn't me! The chances are so fucking extreme, well it couldn't have been me. Wise up. I was sick in bed that day, I had the flu, it was a luxury, there were only three of us.

MILLER You remember being sick that day, that particular day?

O'HARE Well you remember it!

MILLER My brother was blinded!

O'HARE *Pause.* You haven't got a blind brother. You fucken chancer!

MILLER Maybe I have, maybe I haven't. Doesn't make it right!

O'HARE Everyone was at it! You'd be in the back yard minding your own business and this fucking bag of shite would hit you right in the gub.

MILLER Back home, in Switzerland, we have a golf club beside us, sometimes the balls come over and take a window out.

O'HARE You're equating a direct hit with a bag of shite with a fucking golf ball.

MILLER I'm just saying. you can do a lot of damage with a golf ball...

O'HARE Man you gotta get back in the real world! *He stands in front of the badger again.* Snooky! You're vicious wee fuckers when you're cornered, aren't ye? *He shadow boxes with him.* You just don't let go! Grrrrrrr. *He turns.* You know when you have a few pints and you start talking about the old days, you say, do you remember your man who used to stand on the corner shouting Six Lighters A Pound. And the other fella goes, aye, I remember him, Six Lighters a Pound.

MILLER *(singing and playing the blues)* Six Lighters A Pound...

O'HARE ...and do you remember Snowballs, they're like

chocolate and coconut and mallow and you'd buy one and sit on it by mistake...

MILLER   (*singing and playing*) Six Lighters A Pound...

O'HARE   ...and Orange juice used to come in wee pyramids...

MILLER   Six Lighters A Pound...

O'HARE   Shit like that...

MILLER   Six Lighters...

O'HARE   Okay! Enough! If we can't mention crisps we're not going to get away with fucking snowballs and Sukisunkap. Specially if the President of the United States is coming to town, we'd look like we were mental.

MILLER   Six Lighters A Pound...get your, six lighters a pound...*he stops suddenly*...Who said it was the President?

O'HARE   No-one. I just thought, they don't get this panicked about anyone else. They're not going to have us up against a deadline if it's the fucking Israeli ambassador or some cunt from Monte Cristo.

MILLER   The President. Right enough. You'd want to impress him. A new national anthem.

O'HARE   And a badger.

MILLER   And a badger. Bloody hell.

O'HARE   A badger, why a badger?

They both think about it.

MILLER Because not everything here is always black and white.

O'HARE And every once a while you find a body in the middle of the road. *He looks uneasy.* Right. Come on. Focus. The new Northern Ireland.

MILLER What the hell do I know about the new Northern Ireland, haven't been here in twenty years.

O'HARE Not even on tour?

MILLER I always made an excuse. I mean after what I went through, why would I come back?

O'HARE Oh yeah.

(PAUSE)

MILLER I don't like to talk about it. (**Pause**) But everything goes back to that. That day. (**Pause**) Changes you.

O'HARE Yep. Sure it does. Did.

MILLER Yeah, but that was the past, that was the past.

O'HARE *He is at the door; he opens it and peers out.* You hear that?

MILLER What? (*O'Hare shakes his head and closes the door*) In fact I'm sick of talking about it.

O'HARE (*distracted*) What?

MILLER   That day.

O'HARE   So don't...

MILLER   But everything goes back to that, you know? I was piddling about in stupid wee bands...

O'HARE   Really?

MILLER   And then it happened, and it changed who I was, it kind of, kind of reinforced the sanctity of...

O'Hare yawns, and then taps his watch.

O'HARE   Pardon me. But we need to focus, time's a tickin...

MILLER   Okay, alright. Ourselves excluded, give me five famous Ulstermen.

O'HARE   Ulstermen?

MILLER   Northern Irish men. From-the-north-of-Ireland...If we issued a set of stamps, whose faces?

O'HARE   Georgie Best, Hurricane Higgins, Bobby Sands...I don't know.

MILLER   Two drunks and an an eating disorder. *He plays the melody to Would You Go A Pastie Supper Bobby Sands.* What? Post Troubles Irony. (Pause) Remember all that shit? Scary times.

O'HARE   Amazing times, so they were. Our dilemma is how to use it. That sense of unity.

MILLER   Unity?

O'HARE   I mean our lot. Whether you supported the trouble, you supported him, the sacrifice, one life ebbing away, refusing to yield, you want to get that spirit into it, that would inspire you, wouldn't it? Someone who laid down their life for what they believed in. A martyr. I was at the funeral. Man, if you could bottle that.

MILLER   If you could bottle that. (*Pause*) George and Alex would drink it.

O'HARE   We brought an Empire to its knees.

MILLER   Did you really? It's recovered rather well, don't you think? Okay, unity, I go with. But George, he gave unity and pleasure. I don't think your man ever managed that. (*O'Hare gives him a look*) Interesting, you a poet, you didn't mention a poet. Heaney won the Nobel prize, Muldoon the Pullitzer.

O'HARE   You're very well informed for a tinkler.

MILLER   I saw their names on the list. (*O'Hare looks surprised.*) They must have been busy.

O'HARE   Bastards.

MILLER   Ah, God love you, always getting bronze in the iambic pentameter.

O'HARE   I was never part of the Queens' University set. This, this'll be remembered a hundred years after any of that shit, so it will.

MILLER   Optimist. (*He laughs*)

O'HARE What?

MILLER I'd forgotten. So I had.

O'HARE What are you...?

MILLER So we will. So I do. I've been away so long, so I have. I just think about the music, when sometimes the melody is in the words, so it is.

O'HARE You taking the piss?

MILLER No. So I'm not. I'd forgotten the way we add that to everything. So I had. Superfluous words.

O'HARE Ah. Right. Getcha. Never really thought about it. So I haven't.

MILLER Well maybe we should, so we should. The repetitive nature of it is good, so it is.

O'HARE It's an unconscious thing, so it is.

MILLER It's like we don't expect to be believed. I had lunch, so I did. I really did. I can afford lunch. I have it every day.

O'HARE Ah, can you imagine it. If Neil Armstrong was from here? That's one small step for man, so it is.

MILLER I'm on the moon, I really am, so I am. Honestly. You have to believe me, look I have pictures. We'll fight them on the beaches, so we will.

O'HARE   I have a dream, so I have.

MILLER   And I bet you a million bucks, there's some boyo , getting married, biggest day of his life, goes up to the altar, his bride looking gorgeous, the Minister says, do you take this woman to be your lawfully wedded wife and he says...

O'HARE   I do, so I do.

They fall about laughing

MILLER   I do so I do. *He plays, then sings* We're Northern Ireland so we are, We're Northern Ireland, so we are.

O'HARE   *singing* Belfast, Ballymena, Ballywalter, Ballyhalbert...

MILLER   We're Northern Ireland so we are...

O'HARE   Banbridge, Ballyharry, Benburb, Burger King...

MILLER   Burger King...?

O'HARE   I'm strugglin' here!

MILLER   We're Northern Ireland so we are...

They sing together, repeating the line with increasing vigour...and then it slows down, runs out of steam and stops.

O'HARE   That's bollocks.

MILLER   You may have a point. *He sighs, drums his fingers on top of the keyboard, then gets up and stretches* Do you know what we need? Sustenance. You think they'd have provided samiches.

O'HARE   Veda! We have to mention Veda bread!

MILLER   Veda! C'mon. Let's get outta here, lunch and lubrication will speed things along nicely.

He moves across and takes his coat off the hanger and puts it on. He studies his reflection, making sure the coat sits just right.

O'HARE   Out there? Why don't we just order in? We've hardly started.

MILLER   Nah, change a scene, work wonders. I'll buy you a pint. Two if you're good. *O'Hare looks nervously at the door. Miller crosses to him and puts his arm around him. O'Hare stiffens.* C'mon, what's the worst that could happen?

O'Hare hesitates, then takes a deep breath.

O'HARE   Just a wee bit, y'know, agoraphobic.

He pulls the top of his parka up, so that he's well hidden. They cross to the door and exit, with Miller singing;

MILLER   We're Northern Ireland, so we are, we're Northern Ireland so we are...

We hear their steps on the wooden stairs getting quieter as they descend; and then louder as they very quickly return. Miller enters and crosses to the keyboards. O'Hare stands in the doorway.

O'HARE   What?!

Miller stands over the keyboards and picks out a simple melody, which will ultimately become the national anthem. He plays it three times. Then nods to himself, and walks back to the door.

MILLER   Inspiration.

He passes on out past O'Hare and continues down the stairs. O'Hare looks across at the keyboards. Then he shakes his head.

O'HARE   Wanker.

He exits.

The stage is empty, for an uncomfortably long period. Then some might notice the badger move a leg, and then scratch his head. The door opens and the badger freezes. A young woman, SEAN, enters. She has a large handbag over her shoulder, a smart suit, and sunglasses. She is surprised to find the rehearsal room empty.

SEAN   Oh! *She takes out her mobile phone and rapidly calls. As she walks and talks the badger follows her.* They're not here! Yes, I know they're supposed to be here, but as I just said, they're not here. I don't know where they are! If I knew where they where I wouldn't be phoning you to tell you they're not here!

She closes the phone and turns and lets out a shout of surprise when she finds the badger so close. She holds her chest, calms herself, and then moves past it, walking back and forth as she begins to rehearse what she will say when the poet and musician return.

SEAN   Mr. O'Hare, Mr. O'Hare, Desmond, Dessie...I am such a huge fan. Forgive me – Sean Maguire, I'm handling the public relations for this fabulous project. I'm so excited. Mr. O'Hare,

I can't tell you what your work means to me. And to the people of Northern Ireland. It is so evocative, it is so moving and it's so real. It is timeless. Your 'March of the...March of the...' *she stops, forgetting the title, and opens her bag, fishes around and brings out a book.* 'March of the Irish Wilder...beast. Wilderbeest...' *She can't quite pronounce it.* Wilder. Wielder. Wilder...

ALAN   (THE BADGER) Wildebeest!

Sean screams. She begins to rummage in her bag as she backs away.

SEAN   Don't come near...I swear to God!

ALAN   Relax! *Alan removes his badger head.* Christ, it's warm in here! Vill-debeast, it's *vill*-debeast...

SEAN   I'm sorry, you surprised me, ...it was just a shock when you spoke...

ALAN   Well enjoy me while you can, cos I was cast on the understanding that the mouth would remain zipped. Snooky has taken the fifth. *Alan unzips himself and steps out of the badger costume, letting it fall to the floor. He walks around fanning himself, blowing air out of his cheeks.* Oh that's better, that's better...don't let me interrupt...

SEAN   No, no, I'm just...you didn't see them, Mr. O'Hare and...?

ALAN   They went for lunch.

SEAN   Lunch! They haven't time for...

ALAN   Nothing to do with me! Though after what I've

heard, I'm right in your corner.

SEAN   Is it that bad?

ALAN   It's different, but then what do I know? I'm a badger.
I'm a little sett in my ways.

*He winks and moves amongst the props lining the room, picking them
up and trying them out as Sean studies the book in her hand, looking
somewhat confused. He removes a long blackthorn cane, and begins
using it first as a golf putter, then as a sword, moving up and down
behind her...he keeps looking at her to see if she's watching. She isn't...*

SEAN   Vill-de-beest, Vill-de-beest...

Alan stops suddenly.

ALAN   Do you know much about him?

SEAN   No! Neither of them! It's doing my head in, I've a list
as long as your arm to meet and greet, I can't be expected to...

ALAN   Read one, out loud.

SEAN   I haven't time to waste...why out loud?

ALAN   You'll appreciate it more, out loud.

Sean takes off her sunglasses and sets them down on a table behind her.

SEAN   This one? 'The Men Behind the Men Behind the
Men Behind the Wire'?

ALAN   No, flick.

SEAN   'The Gorgeous Lovely Bluebells of Glenarm'?

ALAN   That'll do rightly.

He moves behind her and lifts her sunglasses and slips them into his pocket.

SEAN   'The Gorgeous Lovely Bluebells of Glenarm...

ALAN   '...The Gorgeous Lovely Bluebells of Glenarm/ early March/what with global warning/and stuff/the gorgeous lovely bluebells of Glenarm surprise us all/I count them/one by one/and get lost often/and in the end have to guess how many will satisfy my love/for the lovely gorgeous bluebell of Glenarm.

SEAN   You're a fan!

ALAN   I'm familiar with his work.

SEAN   Nobody in the office had heard of him! The Bluebells....it's so sweet!

ALAN   He is an acquired taste. Like tripe.

SEAN   Tripe?

ALAN   Christ, how old are you?

SEAN   Old en...

ALAN   No, let me guess. You're...twenty, no, twenty one.

SEAN   Lucky.

ALAN   You're...Virgo...

SEAN   Impressive.

ALAN   And you've never heard of tripe? The lining of a sheep's stomach.

SEAN   Oooh-yuk. What on earth...

ALAN   Well I would hesitate to call it a delicacy but it saw us through many a hard winter.

SEAN   *Where*?

ALAN   Where do you think?! Ah never mind. Yousuns, youse think you're underprivileged if there's no McDonalds on every corner. In my day, old McDonald had a farm. Ee, aye, ee aye...

SEAN   What are you *talking* about...?

ALAN   *sighs* You don't remember any of it, do you?

SEAN   Any of what?

ALAN   What we went through to get to the place where you have no idea what we went through.

SEAN   You mean the...all that? Sure that's all over ages ago.

ALAN   You think? You might be surprised. Jesus, if you'd been talking to me twenty years ago, you'd be quaking in your boots.

Coming right up close You've never heard of The Border Fox?

SEAN   You seem to specialise in animal parts. Where u on TV?

ALAN   I was the most feared...! *He stops himself.* Your accent, West Belfast. Or Belfast fucking West as they call it these days. You know, I could probably have you down to a street or two.

SEAN   Yeah, right.

ALAN   Clonard, right?

SEAN   How do you *do* that?

ALAN   Ah, me ol' stompin ground. Maguire your name is? Your dad was a Maguire...

SEAN   Not that it's any of your business, but no, Maguire is my mother's name...

ALAN   And your da...?

SEAN   My mother fulfilled both positions perfectly well, thank you very much. Now if you don't mind I really...

ALAN   I knew the Maguires of Clonard. Fine lookin girls they were...

SEAN   If you insist...

ALAN   Molly, she was the one...

SEAN   That's my ma! Mother, I mean.

There's an awkward silence. He's gazing at her and she's discomfited by it. She consults her notes again.

ALAN   Anything else I can help you with?

SEAN   No. No thank you. Wildebeest. Bluebells. I'm sure... this composer...

ALAN   If you want to call him that...

SEAN   (PANICKED) He isn't...? Have I...

ALAN   No he is, but he isn't if you know what I mean?

SEAN   Not really, no...

ALAN   Just a matter of opinion. But a word of advice...don't mention the thing...

SEAN   Thing-what-thing?

ALAN   The thing thing he's famous for...what happened to him, you know, the the the the the the thing...

SEAN   Oh *that* thing. The massacre.

ALAN   They called it that....

SEAN   They lined them up and they shot them. I have it here in his biography...

ALAN   It was more like an ambush. A successful military operation.

SEAN   Against a showband.

ALAN   It was sending a message. I heard.

SEAN   He survived...

ALAN   A gun jammed and he ran away.

SEAN   Good for him...but I shouldn't mention it...?

ALAN   He doesn't like to talk about it. Apart from his autobiography. And his documentary. And his fucking opera...

SEAN   I'm getting the feeling you don't approve.

ALAN   Me? What does that matter. I'm just a badger.

But Sean's phone rings and she holds up a finger to silence him.

SEAN   Yes? No, I cannot be in two places at one time. Will you just....no...yes...OKAY! YOU'RE THE BOSS. *She closes the phone.* Bitch! Sorry. I have to run. If they come back, make sure they stay. I won't be long.

She hurries to the door.

ALAN   Hey! *She stops.* You look just like your mother.

SEAN   *smiles hesitantly* Make sure they stay.

She exits.

    ALAN   I'll make certain.

(**Fade to black**)

(**Fade up**)

O'HARE is, urgently writing in his notebook. Miller is absent. ALAN appears in the doorway, wearing Sean's sunglasses, and tapping his way in with the blackthorn stick, pretending to be blind.

    ALAN   Is that you, Gary?

    O'HARE   No, I...you're looking for...

    ALAN   I'm looking for my brother!

O'Hare suddenly looks worried...

    O'HARE   He's...not...here...right...now...

    ALAN   Who are you? *He begins to move towards O'Hare.* I'm here to see my brother! Where's my brother?! *Alan taps his way around a chair and moves right up close to O'Hare.* He's supposed to be here! Where is he?!

    O'HARE   Easy, relax, he'll be back...

O'Hare waves his hand in front of Alan's sunglasses

    ALAN   Where is he?!

O'Hare slowly gives him the fingers. There is no response. Until:

Alan whacks him across the head with the stick, lightning fast, and O'Hare goes down. Alan stands over him. He then beats him with the stick. About six times.

ALAN Now who are ya? What've you done with my brother?! Who are ya?!

O'HARE Stop, stop, stop! I'm working with him we're writing the anthem, we're writing the anthem, we're writing the fucking anthem...!

ALAN What's your name?!

O'HARE Dessie O'Hare, O'Hare, O fucking Hare!

Alan stops beating him.

ALAN There used to be an O'Hare lived behind us in Argyle Street.

O'HARE It wasn't me! I'm a poet, I'm a poet, I'm a fucking poet!

ALAN Poet! What sort of a poet?!

O'HARE A poet poet! I'm writing the lyrics...

ALAN Prove it! Sing them!

O'HARE I can't sing it!

He tries to scramble away, but Alan pins him down.

    ALAN   Lemme hear them!

    O'HARE   We....we have mountains...

We have mountains, we have trees/ We have birds and bumble bees!/ We have apples, we have peat/ In the summer we have sleet!

    ALAN   Fuckin' hell...!

    O'HARE   We have bombs and we have trouble/in the winter we have rubble...

    ALAN   Enough! Jesus! Are you writing it for kids...?

    O'HARE   Yes! Let me up, for Godsake let me up!

    ALAN   Where's my brother, what have you done with my brother?!

    O'HARE   Lunch! He's having lunch! We couldn't agree where to go and we split up! But he'll be back, he'll be back in a minute!

Alan hesitates, then extends a hand and pulls him up.

    ALAN   Sorry about that, but us blind, we're easy pickins, know what a mean? Lamp them before they lamp you, hear what I'm sayin'?

    O'HARE   Yes, yes...it was just...

    ALAN   Now, point me in the direction of his ol' joanna...

O'HARE   It's just...

But Alan has already started tapping towards them. A puzzled O'Hare watches as Alan sits on the stool. He begins to play, A horrendous mishmash of discordant notes.

ALAN   Run that past me again.

O'HARE   Run...?

ALAN   The words! The anthem!

O'HARE   We have mountains...

ALAN   (*singing*) We have mountains...

O'HARE   We have trees/We have birds and bumble...look there's no point, please just wait till...

ALAN   Feed me!

O'HARE   Oh for God...We have birds and bumble bees...

ALAN   We have birds and ...*He stops suddenly.* (*Pause*) He's a bit of a cunt, isn't he?

O'HARE   What? Who?

ALAN   The brother. Up his own arse.

O'HARE I don't really know him well enough to...

ALAN   Oh, he's a cunt all right. How can you work with

him? He'll hog the glory, you know that? It'll be his name on the tin, you'll be round the back with the instructions. Musical prodigies we were...

O'HARE   You ah, have a unique style...

ALAN   You really think so?

O'HARE   It's like...jazz...

ALAN   Bollocks! I had it right up to the age of twelve when a brick...

O'HARE   I heard.

ALAN   Blinded me. And affected the old noggin. They said to my ma, Ma, he'll never play the piano...

O'HARE   That's a very, ahm, specific...

ALAN   (Pause) You know, I only knew he was here cause it was on the news.

O'HARE   *high pitched* The news? Our names? *He goes to the window and looks out.* And it said we were here?

ALAN   Why are you worried about groupies?

O'HARE   Ha! Have you seen the likes that comes to poetry?

ALAN   I can't fucking see!

O'HARE   You're better off, believe me!

ALAN   When I mentioned the news, you sounded...scared.

O'HARE   Me? Scared? (*Pause*) Well so would you be. (PAUSE) You know what pisses me off about this place? They never do anything properly. The Sheiks of Araby, they issue a fatwah they hunt you down and you need body guards and you have to move from safe house to safe house and at least you get to sell millions and millions of books. This lot just...

ALAN   They issued a *fatwah*? Against you?

O'HARE   Well it was more a vague kind of threat. I mean, I got outta town, and it's been twenty years, but they never rescinded, never rescinded. They've probably forgotten. They must have forgotten. They've all gone legit.

ALAN   Like the Corleones. What did you do?

O'HARE   Me? Nothing. Well. A contrary opinion. That's what I do! I'm a poet, the conscience of a nation. But none of them, earnest little patriots or God's little soldiers, they never have a sense of humour do they? Did you hear about the Irish suicide bomber?

ALAN   No.

O'HARE   No, neither did I. Bunch a fuckin' chickens.

ALAN   If you don't mind me saying, chasing you out seems like an extreme reaction to a contrary opinion. More like what an informer or a traitor...

O'HARE   I'm no traitor! Take that back!

ALAN   Woah, easy on, easy on!

O'HARE   Sorry...it's just, it's just this place...been away so long...I know its changed...(*Pause*) Where the hell is he? We haven't much time. You must be a little bit proud of him, recognised all over the world.

ALAN   Yeah recognised as a cunty-bollocks. Sure I am. You know who taught him to play?

O'HARE   Wild guess.

ALAN   You're damn right! Nine years old and I already had it. Till that brick came over the wall...I coulda been a composer...

He bashes out more noise on the keyboard. O'Hare reaches over and switches off the power.

O'HARE   Please, I'm getting a migraine.

ALAN   (Pause) Dessie O'Hare. A poet. You're not just winding me up?

O'HARE   Why would I do that? I am. Really. Check it on Wikipedia. I was up all night writing it. *He laughs at how funny he is.*

ALAN   So you write in Irish?

O'HARE   No, no, I never had the inclination. They're translated into Irish. And for that matter (*he mimes spitting*) Ulster-Scots.

ALAN   And you don't actually live here, because you were chased out.

O'HARE   What's your point?

ALAN   My brother has based his entire career on the fact that he was an angel faced little twerp who lucked into surviving an ambush...

O'HARE   I thought is was a massa...

ALAN   ...who got showered with awards and bursaries to apologise for the trauma and make something of himself and he what did he do? He makes fucking *classical* long players with a wee Irish lilt for gullible Yanks. While you write twee little verses for gullible Yanks. This anthem is really going to be something special!

O'HARE   I do not write twee...!

ALAN   The Gorgeous Lovely Bluebells of Glenarm!

O'HARE   So you do know me!

ALAN   Aye, your reputation precedes you. The Gorgeous Lovely...

O'HARE   That was a one off! Most of them are about the, the, the, the, hell of living through a civil...

ALAN   The hell? You skedaddled!

O'HARE   I was chased...!

ALAN   It was a career move!

O'HARE   Well it didn't fucking work! (*Pause*) Until now. This is my moment. Recognition.

A phone rings. It is conveniently placed on top of an amp by the keyboards, immediately beside Alan. They both look at it. Alan smiles at O'Hare, waiting for him to move, but also knowingly. His hand moves towards it...

ALAN   *He feels his way towards it and lifts it.* Yep? Dessie O'Hare? The poet fella? Sure he's here. Who wants him? Sean? Hold on.

Alan holds out the receiver. It has a long, curly flex. O'Hare very hesitantly takes it. As he walks away with it to speak privately, with his back to Alan, Alan very deliberately brings his fingers down, cutting the line.

O'HARE   H..hello? *He suddenly turns back to Alan, terrified.* It's dead!

ALAN   You sure? *He takes it back and listens* Right enough. Y'all right there matey?

O'HARE   Yes! He actually asked for me?

ALAN   No.

O'HARE   But you...

ALAN   Wasn't a he.

O'HARE   You said Sean.

ALAN   *She* said Sean.

O'HARE   She said Sean? And she didn't shay, say anything else?

ALAN   She was hard to make out, there was some kind of alarm going off in the background.

O'HARE   An alarm?! What kind of...?

ALAN   I don't know! An alarm. She just wanted to know if you were here.

O'HARE   Christ Almighty...!

ALAN   There you go again...

O'HARE   What?

ALAN   Fear. Your voice, goes high pitched.

O'HARE   It does not!

ALAN   You're probably sweating as well...

O'HARE   *wiping at his brow* Your oul bollocks...

ALAN   Aye, them too. *He raises his open hand, and closes it into a fist.* Contraction. I'm like Daredevil. I lost my sight and all my other senses were magnified. You're scared to death...

O'HARE   I'm...

ALAN   You're a squeaky, sweaty, grape nutted yellow belly.

O'HARE   What are you *on*...?! I don't need this! Fuck! *He turns* *back to the window.* They couldn't give me a single day.

ALAN   Hey, c'mon, you're worrying about nothing. Who's gonna bear a grudge for twenty years over a contrary opinion? (PAUSE) I wonder if she's beautiful?

O'HARE   Who?

ALAN   Sean. In movies female assassins are always beautiful.

O'HARE   Don't say that!

ALAN   It's a complement.

O'HARE   Howse it a fucking complement?

ALAN   Only important people get assassinated. No common or garden murder for you.

Alan mimics a gunshot to the head.

O'HARE   Stop it! Please! I want to go home!

ALAN   You're not going to run away now! This is your big chance!

The phone begins to ring again...O'Hare lets out a yelp.

ALAN   Do you want me to...?

O'HARE   No! Don't touch it! *The ringing stops abruptly. O'Hare stares at the phone. He slumps down against the wall. He wipes his arm across his brow.* Sorry, look, look, I'm here for the lyric, for the anthem, you're right, nobody knows about the past, nobody cares, everything is absolutely fine and dandy, it's just the work, the pressure, the time limit...I'm fine, I'm good, I'm perfectly all right.

ALAN   I'm off now.

O'HARE   Don't leave me! *O'Hare jumps to his feet.* Really, seriously, he'll be back in a wee tick, just, just, wait till he comes back, catch up, he'll be dyin to see you...

ALAN   He's had his chance. But will you do something for me...?

O'HARE   Absolutely...

ALAN   Tell him I was here, and give him this:

He gives him the finger.

Fade to black.

Fade up.

O'Hare is still on the floor by the window, writing in a notebook, but then tearing the pages out, balling and tossing. He stops as he hears footsteps coming up the stairs. They stop. He stares at the door. The handle moves down. But the door is locked. O'Hare moves across as it is rattled again..

O'HARE   Not today thanks!

MILLER   Open the bloody door!

O'Hare unlocks it; Miller comes in carrying a large box, tied with a bow.

O'HARE   Where the hell have you been?!

MILLER   Do you have any idea how far I had to walk to find a pastie? Panacotta and panini on every corner, but ask for a pastie and they look at you like you're a fucking space cadet. (BEAT) What's the door locked for?

O'HARE   Security, what do you think? What'd you buy?

MILLER   I didn't buy anything, it was sitting outside the door.

He walks forward with it, and sets it down on a low table, centre-stage. He moves away in order to hang up his coat with the usual thoroughness. O'Hare examines the box, then moves his ear up close.

O'HARE   It's ticking.

MILLER   Clocks will do that.

O'HARE   Ticking.

MILLER   Time, the gift that keeps taking away. When you've done as many charity gigs as I have...

O'HARE   Ticking...

MILLER   ...you get used to their homely little gifts. There's a card wedged into the side there.

O'Hare pulls it out and reads it silently:

O'HARE   Christ.

MILLER   Oh for... give it...*He takes it from O'Hare.'* Thanking you in advance for your contribution. I hope it's a blast. Love, Sean.

O'HARE   See?

MILLER   See what? It's from the Department of Thank-yous.

O'HARE   It's ticking!

MILLER   *Time's* a ticking. Plane to catch! It's a crappy gift, ignore it, let's get busy.

O'HARE   Presents don't tick. If it was a present, there'd be two of them.

MILLER   We're a team. We can share it, six months each. Maybe there's two inside. Open it.

O'HARE   Fuck OFF!

MILLER   What's the problem?

O'HARE   It's ticking!

MILLER   I'll open it.

O'HARE   No!

MILLER   Christ! Can we just get on with this?

O'HARE   It's a bomb.

MILLER   Right. A time bomb.

O'HARE   Don't you see?! It makes perfect sense. They killed soldiers and cops and politicians and civilians, now just when you thought it was safe to go back in the water they're taking one last gasp, they're targeting us. It's the artists who define a nation, and now they're trying to bomb us in the very act of definition.

MILLER   That must be it. Or it could just be a clock! Get a grip!

Miller crosses to the keyboards and gets behind them. O'Hare looks doubtfully down at the box.

O'HARE   You're just going to...? You of all people? Who survived a massa...

MILLER   Listen to this:

He plays the melody he began before lunch. O'Hare's attention is finally deflected and he crosses to the keyboard.

O'HARE   You just...

MILLER   Worked on it over lunch.

O'HARE   Okay...let me...
He lifts his notebook and begins to mumble his lyrics along to the music...

MILLER   What's that...?

O'HARE   We have mountains...We have mountains, we have

trees/ We have birds and bumble bees!/ We have apples, we have peat/In the summer we have sleet...

MILLER   *stopping* Bloody hell.

O'HARE   What?

MILLER   I mean, bloody hell.

O'HARE   It works. It works! That wee melody, it fuckin stuck in me head...come on...from the top...

MILLER   From the top! Listen to you...

O'HARE   Just do it! Come on! We can nail this...! We have mountains...We have mountains, we have trees/ We have birds and bumble bees!/ We have apples, we have peat/In the summer we have sleet...We have bombs and we have trouble/in the winter we have rubble...

MILLER   Jesus!

O'HARE   Is it the melody?

MILLER   No! The Department of Thankyous hear those lyrics, they will be leaving us a fucking bomb.

O'HARE   It's the best I can...you can't guarantee when the inspiration is going to strike .

MILLER   Well according to your contract, you pretty much have to.

O'HARE Who ever kept to a contract? We're artists!

MILLER For hire!

O'HARE Exactly! I got paid up front. Cash in hand outta the Government is no mean feat.

MILLER For which you gave up...

O'HARE I gave up *nothing*.

MILLER That's right. They sent you a contract. Did you even read it?

O'HARE What's the point?

MILLER The point is royalties.

O'HARE *Royalties?*

MILLER They wanted to withhold the copyright. They didn't want to pay royalties. I had it put back into mine. Every time some wee bugger sings our anthem, I get whatever I get.

O'HARE And what do I get?!

MILLER The thanks of a grateful nation!

O'HARE You said you were doing it to give something back! You came on like a fucking charity!

MILLER Charity begins at home.

O'HARE   Fuck! I'm getting my people on to this!

MILLER   You have people?

O'HARE   No! Fuck!

MILLER   Sometimes you have to play hard to get. They've been after me to do this for eight months, this was the only day I had free.

O'HARE   They called me on Tuesday! How's that fair?! Royalties! You have a word with them, you tell them, we're on equal terms or there's no anthem, we'll down tools...

MILLER   I don't get involved in the business end, my agent...

O'HARE   Oi doin't get involved in the business end, fuckin hell, your brother was right, you are a cunty-bollocks...(*Miller looks surprised*) Yeah, he was here, filled me in on a few home truths, so he did.

MILLER   Uhuh, I'm sure he did, except...*I don't have a brother*, you frickin eejit.

O'HARE   Alan who taught you the flute! You were talking about him this morning!

MILLER   I was winding you up!

O'HARE   He came to see you! Your brother, Alan! He remembered me from Argyll Street!

MILLER   Do I sound like I come from fucking Argyll Street?!

O'HARE Then how did you know I lived on the other side and clodded rocks?!

MILLER Because you never stop talking about it on the fucking internet! I looked you up! I'd never heard of you before!

O'HARE You'd never...

MILLER I live in Switzerland! I can't keep up with every third rate poet who...

O'HARE Shut up! Just...shut up. It was your brother. Your brother Alan. (Pause) You don't have a brother.

MILLER No!

O'HARE You were winding me up?

MILLER Yes.

O'HARE So how do I know you're not winding me up *now*?

MILLER You don't. But I'm not. Swear to God.

O'Hare turns slowly and looks at the box.

O'HARE I've walked into their trap. Don't you see? There is no national anthem, what do we need a national anthem for? We're not a country, we're an artificial creation, we have no identity, no unity, no future, why the fuck would we need to sing about it? We don't exist. I spoke out, and they never forgot, and now they've lured me back in and have me where they want me, sitting here, with a bomb about to go off.

MILLER   Yer ma's yer da.

O'HARE   *What?*

MILLER   I've met plenty of self centred, egotistical eeijits in my time, most of them play the cello, but you're the best yet. What're you saying, you expressed an opinion twenty years ago, and they've given up their guns, and gone into government, and cleaned up their act, but your opinion had such an impact that nobody ...

O'HARE   You don't know them. They never forget. They're the elephants of terrorism!

MILLER   So never mind the soldiers and the cops and the internment and the shoot to kill and the hunger strikes, they're more concerned about someone who never quite conquered iambic ...

O'HARE   Yes! Yes! Yes! And it's still ticking, it's still ticking ...we could just run away. But they know that. If we make a move for the door they'll just trip it and...that means they're listening... watching...they're playing with us! *They both look warily around the room. Whispering*: Where's the fucking badger?

MILLER   Snooky

O'HARE   He was here...here, right here...Badgers don't just... walk off...

MILLER   (Pause) What am I even doing giving this the time of day?! Jesus! It's a stuffed badger! It had a purpose unlike...Jesus! And that, you spastic, it a clock! It's a gift! And if they wanted to take you out, you don't think they've the wherewithal to take you out in fucking Galway?!

O'HARE   *Pause* Good point.

MILLER   See? There's nothing to worry...

O'HARE   You're absolutely right. They're not after me. They're after *both of us.*

MILLER   Ah for Jesus... why would they want to kill me? What have I done?

O'HARE   I don't know! Maybe it's a life time achievement award.

MILLER   It's a box with a clock!

O'HARE   What about Alan?

MILLER   So there's a lunatic on the loose who claims he's my brother. When you get to my position, you attract crazy people.

O'HARE   What position's that? Because when you start as an arsehole, where else is there to go?

MILLER   How would you know if I started as an arsehole, even though I'm not?

O'HARE   How would I know?

MILLER   How would you know?

O'HARE   How would I know?

MILLER   I'm hearing an echo.

O'HARE   Always an arsehole, and when this goes off, that's all will be left of you. One big exploded arsehole.

MILLER   What's your problem exactly?

O'HARE   What's my problem?

MILLER   Jesus change the record!

O'HARE   At least I can! I'll tell you what my problem is. I have a problem with swans.

MILLER   Swans?

O'HARE   Swans.

MILLER   Swans?

O'HARE   Swans.

MILLER   I'm pining for Alan.

O'HARE   Swans.

MILLER   Is it their big necks?

O'HARE   Wild Swans.

MILLER   Wild swans?

O'HARE   *The*...Wild Swans.

MILLER   *The*...Wild...Swans...

O'HARE   Penny starting to drop?

MILLER   The Wild Swans?

O'HARE   The Wild Swans.

MILLER   My first band! The Wild Swans! Cool name, wasn't it? Before that we called ourselves The Synthenatti Kids. You must have been a fan?

O'HARE   Yeah right.

MILLER   Okay. Not a crime. You were probably still into punk.

O'HARE   I wasn't into punk, and don't pretend you don't remember.

MILLER   Remember what?

O'HARE   You're funny.

MILLER   You're funny what?

O'HARE   You're so fucking...

MILLER   I can't remember every fan who ever...!

O'HARE   I wasn't a fan! (*Quietly*) The audition.

MILLER   The what?

O'HARE   The audition!

MILLER   What audition?

O'HARE   The audition were you were auditioning for singers and I came in and sang and I broke my heart singing my lyrics and you just laughed and said next! Like you were some big fucking bigshot instead of some fucking geek boy in his mum's garage with your wavy hair and Argos synth. And I was so cut up I didn't write another thing for two years, that's what you did for me you arrogant self centred limelight hogging up your own arse fucking...Proddie bastard.

MILLER   The heart of the matter...!

O'HARE   You know something?

MILLER   I know plenty!

O'HARE   I should open the box and do the world a fucking favour! Save us all from another set of lousy elevator music!

MILLER   You're just pathetic. Well do you know something...?

O'HARE   I know plenty!

MILLER   ...maybe I did the world a favour not picking you if it saved us from two years of your fucking limericks! Why don't you piss off back to your twelve in a fucking bed hovel!

O'HARE   Six!

MILLER   And the fact is, you fucking dick – I don't remember you, I auditioned hundreds of singers, so you were as insignificant then as you are now...

O'HARE   Fuck off!

O'Hare takes a swing at him. Miller ducks and grabs him and head butts him in the stomach. As he goes down O'Hare takes hold of Miller and they both fall to the ground and begin to wrestle.

O'HARE   I'm going to kill you, you fucking...

MILLER   Not before I kill you, you fucking...

Miller begins to pound O'Hare's head relentlessly into the floor.

MILLER   I got out of here because of grudge bearing little gutter snipes like you! Wild horses wouldn't drag me back!

O'HARE   What about Wild Swans you fucking talentless...

He bucks under him and throws him off, he dives on top of Miller and begins pounding his head on the floor. He takes hold of Miller's hand and begins to bend it back.

MILLER   No! Don't! Please God don't! Not the hands!

The clock alarm goes off suddenly – they both stop and stare at it.

SUDDEN BLACK.

The alarm clock continues to sound in darkness, now joined by:

MILLER & O'HARE   Aghhhhhhhhhhhhhhhh!

The clock alarm sounds. Lights go up on MILLER and O'HARE curled together in a ball on the floor, hugging each other for protection.

MILLER & O'HARE   Aghhhhhhhhhhhhhhhh!

Just as the door opens, the alarm stops. SEAN stands in the doorway surveying the scene, a large handbag looped over her arm. There's a long moment of frozen horror from the pair of them, and then Miller suddenly rolls away and bounces to his feet, flexing his muscles.

MILLER   ...and that is how William McCreagh won the All Ireland Wrestling Championship in 1982. A triumph of physical dexterity over pure strength...Ha! We have a visitor...!

Miller begins to move towards Sean, but she brushes past him and advances on O'Hare, who is just standing up. He immediately backs away. But then Sean puts out her hand...

SEAN   – Mr. O'Hare, Mr. O'Hare, Desmond, Dessie...I am such a huge fan. Forgive me – Sean Maguire, I'm handling the public relations on this fabulous project. I'm so excited. *They shake hands.* Mr. O'Hare, I can't tell you what your work means to me. And to the people of Northern Ireland.   It is so evocative, it is so moving and it's so real. It is timeless. And do you know also, although I shouldn't really be saying this, I believe the President of the United States himself was instrumental in having your name elevated above those of others who shall remain nameless but who lobbied incessantly for this most prestigious undertaking. *She turns to Miller and extends her hand.* Mr. Miller – my granny loves your music. Every Christmas I know exactly what to get her – one of Gary Miller's...long players she calls them. Of course she wouldn't know a download from a... whatever...now isn't this exciting! How's it all going?

Miller and O'Hare look frostily at each other.

MILLER   We're making progress.

SEAN   It would be a real thrill if I could hear some of it.

O'HARE   Not that much progress.

MILLER   We're nearly there.

SEAN   Well I'm sure it's wonderful. And you'll be done by five?

O'HARE   Ish.

SEAN   It'll have to be. Time to rehearse the orchestra, the choir, the choreography...

MILLER   Choreography?

SEAN   Yes we have six hundred Irish dancers...

MILLER   That would be Northern Irish dancers...

SEAN   ...just waiting to...

O'HARE   Like *Riverdance*?

MILLER   Lagan Dance.

SEAN   And a visual depiction of the history of Ireland...

MILLER   Northern Ireland...

SEAN   Which will not airbrush out the tragic aspects of our history...

O'HARE   The hunger strikes...

MILLER   Shankhill bombing...

O'HARE   Bloody Sunday...

MILLER   Omagh...

O'HARE   The Plantation of Ulster...

MILLER   Build yourself a time machine!

SEAN   But we will primarily celebrate everything that is good and wonderful about the place we call home.

O'Hare and Miller look bashfully away. Miller reaches behind his keyboard and takes out a set of headphones. He offers them to Sean.

MILLER   Here, have a listen.

Sean sets down her hand bag and takes the earphones.

SEAN   Thank-you, thank-you, how exciting!

Miller presses a button for her to listen. She begins to nod along, nodding approvingly at them...

MILLER   Loud enough?

SEAN   What?!

He shakes his head and gives her the thumbs up. Then turns to O'Hare.

MILLER   Are you falling for this?

O'HARE   For what?

MILLER   For her. Blowing smoke up your arse.

O'HARE   Yeah right.

MILLER   Yeah wrong. There's something not right about this.

O'HARE   About what?

MILLER   This! Her!

O'HARE   What're you talking about?

MILLER   She blanked me. You saw it. Totally. For eight months they've been falling all over their own arses trying to lure me in...they virtually offered me a Knighthood...

O'HARE   You?

MILLER   Yes! Services to...

O'HARE   *You*?

MILLER   Ah, come off it, if they offered you, you'd bite their...

O'HARE   How dare you! I might have run, but I'm no...nice to be offered, though, nice to be...if this anthem...

SEAN   *singing along, out of tune* 'We have mountains, we have trees, We have birds and bumble bees!

MILLER   And then she breezes in and she's all over you and she blanks me and do you know why...

O'HARE   Good taste is...

MILLER   Because she has no idea who I am! Because she doesn't care! Because she's after you...

O'HARE   Me?

MILLER   The bomb! It didn't go off! She's here to finish the job!

O'HARE   Och balls!

MILLER   Man, God, use your head. We have no idea who she is!

O'HARE   She's...

MILLER   How do we know! The bomb didn't go off, only the alarm, it went on for ever...she's come to re-set the timer, or a gun in her handbag. Look at the size of it.

SEAN   We have apples, we have peat, in the summer we have sleet!

MILLER   Check her bag!

O'HARE   You check her bag!

SEAN   *hesitantly* We have bombs and we have trouble...in the winter we have rubble...Oh this won't do.

O'HARE   Oh this won't do?

SEAN   We have bombs? We have rubble?

O'HARE   That's what we got.

SEAN   We can't have bombs and rubble! We're selling something here!

O'HARE   We will not airbrush out the tragic aspects of our history!

MILLER   You said it!

He makes a sudden grab for her bag.

SEAN   What are you doing?!

MILLER   I'm exposing you for what you are!

She grabs it back. He takes hold of one handle. She maintains a grip on the other. They pull back and forth.

MILLER   Let go of it!

SEAN   It's my bag! I understand the pressures you're working under, but...

O'HARE   Give her the bag, wouldja?! Jesus, paranoid or what?

MILLER   Me? You've been ravin' since...

SEAN   Just give it to me!

MILLER   What are you *hiding*?

SEAN   I'm not hiding nothin!

MILLER   I'm not hiding nothin! Ta-da! You're not in PR!

O'HARE   Will you leave her a-fucking-lone!

MILLER   She's one of them! Where's your bullshit detector, man? Now give me the...

He rips the bag from her grasp, and its contents spill across the floor.

SEAN   Now look what you've done, you stupid bastard!

O'Hare and Miller both stare at her.

MILLER   Ta-da!

SEAN   I'm sorry. I don't know what came...Look. It's my favourite bag. You're right. I'm not really in PR. I've been seconded because everyone who *is* in PR is tied up with more important...I'm in Human Resources. I'm sorry. I'm doing my best. Look, look, here's my ID...

MILLER   *looking away* Fake!

SEAN   It *is not*! If it was fake I'd have a decent hair cut.

Miller continues to look away; she shows it to O'Hare; he looks horrified.

MILLER   I don't trust her! And what the fuck is this?

He kneels and picks something up from the spilled contents of the bag.

SEAN   A fork.

MILLER   But what's it for? Eh, jabbing, jabbing, that's what it's for!

SEAN   Yes it is.

MILLER   Your bomb didn't go off and you're reduced to jabbing us! You stainless steel rat!

O'HARE   Why the fork?

MILLER   Why the fork?!

SEAN   Just...protection, all right? In case I'm attacked.

MILLER   Why would you be attacked!

SEAN   Because men do that!

MILLER   Bollocks!

He grabs her and holds the fork to her neck.

O'HARE   Let her go.

MILLER   I'm protecting you too!

O'HARE   Let her go!

MILLER   No! Search her!

O'HARE   Oh for fuck...

He grabs Miller's fork hand and twists it back. Miller lets out a scream and lets go of Sean and the fork, but then they both begin to wrestle, almost dancing across the stage. Sean crosses to the box and bends over it. Miller and O'Hare both notice at the same time.

SEAN   This isn't what I ordered.

She puts her hands on it and prepares to lift off the top.

MILLER & O'HARE   No!

She freezes. Miller and O'Hare scramble across the stage towards her. They skid to a halt on their knees on either side of her.

SEAN   It was supposed to be wine but...

She makes another attempt to remove the top...

MILLER & O'HARE   No!

MILLER   Hooks for hands...!

SEAN   Don't be silly, it's from our department, it's just not what I...

She suddenly whips the top off...O'Hare and Miller duck down...and we see two alarm clocks, connected by a series of wires...they recover slowly and stare at them, dumbstruck...

SEAN   I didn't order clocks.

O'HARE   Fuuuuuck...

MILLER   ...ing hell...

SEAN   Why would they be wired together?

She reaches forward to try and separate them...

MILLER & O'HARE   No! Jesus!

They each grab one of her hands...

SEAN   What are you doing? Let go of...

O'HARE   Listen to me, it's a bomb...you know, bang, limbs fly in opposite directions...

SEAN   It's not a...

MILLER   What do you think *that* is, Highland Toffee...?

O'HARE   Semtex!

SEAN   What...?

MILLER   Oh for the love of God, kids today...

O'HARE   Plastic explosive...

SEAN   *Plastic*...?

MILLER   Not in a good way.

O'HARE   It's a bomb, love.

SEAN   A *bomb*? A *bomb* bomb? Why would...why would... oh my...sweet Jesus...a bomb...this is just...surreal...

O'HARE   The Surreal IRA.

SEAN   We have to get...

She starts to get up, O'Hare keeps her firmly in place.

O'HARE   No!

MILLER   *No?*

O'HARE   Whoever was listening to us before, is listening to us now. We try to leave and kaboom.

O'Hare and Sean look around them, paranoid. Miller stares at Sean.

MILLER   Unless...

O'HARE   Unless...?

MILLER   She's just toying with us. Be careful what you wish for. You wanted our first intentional suicide bomber, now...

SEAN   That's just ridic...

MILLER   Stop messing with our heads! What have we done?! We're artists!

SEAN   I haven't...

MILLER   You're only young! You have your whole life ahead of you in our brave new world! Why throw it away on us...!

SEAN   What is wrong with you?! It's a bomb, a bomb!

O'HARE We know what it is! Jesus!

MILLER You thought there was a bogeyman out there and you let a banshee come in the front door. (*to Sean*) You're a pawn in somebody else's game. Brainwashed from birth.

SEAN   This has nothing to do with me! I work for the Government! Blowing three people to bits is not a worthwhile use of Human Resources! I know it looks like a bomb, but but but maybe it's not...it can't be, not in this day and...It's just an elaborate hoax. Someone is playing a trick on you.

O'HARE Heaney!

MILLER Oh for fuck...

O'HARE Mind games. Look at the wires.

MILLER I'm looking at the wires!

O'HARE Red, white and blue. It's a message. They're telling me I sold them out to the Brits, I went over to the other side...

MILLER That's just crazy bollocks, there was nothing left to sell! We got off the sinking ship. And they don't do bomb wire in green white and...!

O'HARE They're after me!

SEAN It's a hoax! It has to be...! Youse aren't that important! Look, I'll take a wire...

She reaches forward and takes hold of one...

MILLER and O'HARE No!!!

SEAN I have it and heaven help me I'm going to pull, so you may as well take the other ones...

MILLER No fucking...

SEAN TAKE THEM! Please. Please. It's the only way we're going to know.

Miller takes it. She looks at O'Hare...

O'HARE This is madness! Shit!

He reaches out and takes hold of the third wire.

MILLER Now what?

SEAN Count to three...?

They nod.

MILLER Okay, one...

O'HARE Two...

They both look away...

SEAN   Wait...

O'HARE   Wait! Jesus! What?!

SEAN   If, and I mean if, and it's not, I know it's not, but if it is...and it...we can't just blink out of existence without...you know...

MILLER   Thank you God.

SEAN   Making our peace with...upstairs...

O'HARE   Jesus!

SEAN   Yes! If there's anything you have to say...say it...say it now...

MILLER   No, no, no, no, no, no...that's just exactly what you want! She's still screwing with our heads...!

SEAN   Would you ever get over yourself! I don't care who you are or what you've done...

MILLER   I haven't done...

SEAN   ...I'm just saying if you have some final words they might as well be honest ones...

MILLER   ...I haven't done anything!

O'HARE   I did sell them out! *They both look at him.* I didn't mean to. I just have a big mouth.

MILLER   You sold them out by *mistake*?

O'HARE There was drink involved. There were tourists involved. You big yourself up and in the bigging, and the fibbing, I inadvertently gave someone away, who gave someone a way. I'm not an informer, I just like a bit of gossip. (*Pause, to Miller*) You?

MILLER What do you want me to say? The affairs? The beatings?

O'HARE and SEAN Yes!

MILLER I haven't! I have a lovely family! I make music! It gives pleasure to millions! Everything is perfect! If I've anything to say it's than-you God for a wonderful life!

O'HARE Pride comes before...!

MILLER It's not pride, it's...!

SEAN I don't want to die a virgin! *O'Hare and Miller stop their bickering to stare at Sean. She swallows, looks down, gives a little shrug.* So, what's your problem?

O'HARE No problem, this day and age it's a fricken miracle.

SEAN It goes no further than this room.

MILLER Unlike ourselves.

O'HARE Fucking hell.

MILLER Fucking hell.

SEAN Fucking hell.

They stare at the bomb. Then slowly they nod.

O'HARE One.

MILLER Two.

SEAN Three!

They each look away and pull...and at the same time the door behind them crashes open...causing everyone to jump. But there is no explosion. Instead ALAN enters in his badger suit, but minus the head, wearing sunglasses.

ALAN Gotcha now!

SEAN You! God! You nearly gave me a...

ALAN You be quiet sweetheart, it's not you I'm after.

He crosses the room, producing a gun, and looms over O'Hare

O'HARE *Alan?*

He puts his hands up.

MILLER What's going on? What do you...?

ALAN Shut the fuck up! *He whacks Miller with the butt of the gun. He tumbles forward, clutching his head. He turns to O'Hare, who cowers down.*

O'HARE Don't hit me!

ALAN   I'm not going to hit you. *O'Hare breathes a sigh of relief* I'm going to shoot you through the back of the head like the dog you are.

He puts the gun to O'Hare's head.

O'HARE   Please. I'm sorry.

ALAN   What're you sorry for?

O'HARE   Whatever you want me to be!

ALAN   Not good enough! Be...fucking...specific...

O'HARE   I'm sorry for...saying things...that might have been construed...

ALAN   Construed!

Now he does get whacked; as he holds his head, Alan spins towards Miller, who is just beginning to rise...

ALAN   Where do you think you're going?

MILLER   *groggily* My taxi is...

ALAN   Siddown! *Miller sits.*

MILLER   I'm sorry, there seems to be some kind of.... misunder...

ALAN   Is that right, is that fucking right?

MILLER   Yes, I...

ALAN   Are you not the composer, Gary Miller?

MILLER   Yes, I...

ALAN   Did you not have five million selling albums...

MILLER   Six if you count...

ALAN   SHUT UP! Tell me, *Gary Miller*, what happened to you twenty years, ago, what happened out on that country road, that *incident*, that *massacre*...

MILLER   I don't like to talk...

ALAN   I'll tell you *your* version of what happened. Youse were lined up, five Ulster prods in Bandit Country, and youse were shot one by one till they came to you, and they told you to get on your knees, and you said no, you were gonna die standin up, and they said fair enough and pulled the trigger, but the gun jammed and you took off and they came after ya...but you survived, and said you were gonna dedicate your life to the memory of the fallen, and to music...

MILLER   Yes, that's roughly...

ALAN   Why don't you tell us what really happened?

MILLER   I did, it's, it's, it's on record, my book, my...

ALAN   Tell us!

MILLER   I don't know what you want me to...

ALAN   The truth! Sure, you were last in line, sure you were told to get on your knees, but what did you say, you wanted to die standing up? *Miller starts to nod*...Bollocks! You got on your knees and you cried like a baby, you begged for your life...

MILLER   No, I'm sure I...

ALAN   ...and the gun was put to your head, but it didn't jam, did it?

MILLER   Yes it...

ALAN   You started singing. Singing. What did you sing?

MILLER   I don't...

ALAN   *singing* Sinne Fianna Fil, A t fé gheall ag Éirinn,

O'HARE   The Solider's Song...?

ALAN   Shut up! *Back to Miller.* The Soldier's Song? In fucking Irish?

MILLER   I...wanted to live...

O'HARE   How the hell did you know...?

ALAN   Shut up! *Back to Miller* How did you know it?

MILLER   We were in a showband! If we were in a protestant club we had to play the national anthem at the end of every show, if we were in a Republican area...you had to adapt...so we sang the Irish...it didn't mean anything...

ALAN   And you sewed enough doubt that the others said, he could be one of us, let him live, let him crawl away... crying and droolin and snortin...big hero, yeah? Big fucking hero...

MILLER How...how do you know this...?

ALAN   How do you think I know it?! Do you not recognise my voice...?

MILLER Oh Jesus no!

ALAN   Oh Jesus yes! Traitor to your own kind! Bad enough, but then you're lauded and applauded and you got the breaks and scholarships...and suddenly you're not in a showband anymore, you're a *composer*, and how did you repay the fallen? You took every single fucking Irish classic and *reinterpreted* them into five fucking muzak monstrosities...

MILLER I wouldn't necessarily describe them as...

ALAN   Which the Government used on *me*!

MILLER *On* you...what're you...

ALAN   On me! In solitary! They tried to break me by piping you in every day for six months! 24 hours a day! Do you hear me?

MILLER Yes!

ALAN   I have tinnitus with the panpipes of the fucking Andes in it!

MILLER   But that has nothing to do...

ALAN   I had no wish to hear the *Londonderry Air* with a fucking bleatin llama! Do you understand?! They did not break me. They DID NOT break me, but I could not concentrate, couldn't think, couldn't plan my revenge on...*he turns suddenly as O'Hare is just starting to rise*...this BASTARD who sold me down the river...

O'HARE   I did not...

ALAN   SHUT UP! *Turning back to Miller* But I'll tell ya, it helped crystallize one thing – I swore to every God there is that I'd track you down and finish the job I started and that you weaselled out of...and by God it's taken me twenty years for the stars to align, twenty years to get all three of you in one room.

SEAN   Thee of us? What're you talking...

ALAN   What do you think I'm talking about?!

SEAN   I don't know! How would I...what's going on...who are you people...what's wrong with you...

ALAN   Listen to me...

SEAN   I'm in human resources...

ALAN   You're here for a reason...

SEAN   I'm here to make sure these two...

ALAN   You're here because I called in favours, sure half my lads are in Government now...

SEAN   Your...

ALAN   Molly Maguire, prettiest girl in all of West Belfast. Molly Maguire, mother to Sean Maguire, Sean Maguire, never knew her da...

SEAN   No...

ALAN   ...no name on the birth certificate, expunged from the record books...

SEAN   No...

ALAN   Sean Maguire with the little birth mark on the inside of her arm...

SEAN   But...*tearfully* but...but...you're...you're our *badger*... Daddy?

She moves closer to him; she wipes at her tears, she reaches out and gently strokes the arm with the birthmark...

ALAN   Darlin, all the times I wanted to...

Sean suddenly looks at her fingers. The birth mark is rubbing off...

ALAN   I was on the run,...and I snuck back...but they were waiting for me because I'd been sold down the river by this man... *he whacks O'Hare with the gun*...They ripped you from my arms, and they put me away, and your mother wanted nothing more to do with me, but I've watched you, I've been your guardian angel. Your first bike, communion, I was there, I got you your job. Do you ever wonder how bullies at school faded away, how boyfriends never dared lay a finger on you? And it's all been leading up to *this*...this day, this day of vengeance!

SEAN   Couldn't we just have gone for coffee?

ALAN   No! You have to see me in my element, doing what I do. You have to understand the legacy, the legacy your mother stopped you from inheriting. Darlin? Don't you see? You're the daughter of a warrior, an Irish pure bred, one gene from ginger, as unsullied as the Queen of Heaven herself. You'll join me, I'll train ye, we can turn the tide? We kill these two, we get clean away...we re-start the war!

SEAN   No!

ALAN   This is what I am! I'm the last of the Mohicans...

SEAN   No, if I'm...if I'm...then you're only the second last of the Mohicans...And I don't, I won't allow this...Oh Jesus Christ... Why does it always have to be about the past?!

ALAN   Because that's all we have!

SEAN   What about the future?

ALAN   Our future is our past!

SEAN   Not for me! I'm twenty one! I don't remember any of that stuff!

ALAN   What kind of an excuse is that! FUCKING LEARN IT! Your mother denied me, denied it all, everything we fought for. And she wasn't alone! My people, my PEOPLE. They gave up everything for...for...for nothing! Those bastards, those BASTARDS just gave up! Both sides, every side, they sat down with their cups of tea, and because they were all a bit tired of it they sold us down the river!

SEAN   We got peace...

ALAN   But nothing was decided! Nobody won! In every war there has to be a victor! And we had none! We had compromise! Compromise is democracy built on a swamp!

SEAN   No! You drain the swamp! That's...what...democracy is...

ALAN   It's wallpaper over a gaping stench hole! It festers and in a generation we'll be shooting the heads off my grand children, your kids, all over again!

SEAN   No we won't...we've changed...we've all changed. We believe in harmony, we believe in peace and a permanent end to violence.

ALAN   That's just pathetic. You're a child, you know nothing about...

SEAN   We believe in harmony, we believe in peace and a permanent end to violence.

ALAN   Biscuit tin slogans!

She is traumatised, she slips to her knees, weeping...

SEAN   We believe in harmony, we believe in peace...

ALAN   No, darling please...!

SEAN   ...and a permanent end to violence...

ALAN   You're my daughter and you will inherit...!

SEAN   We believe in harmony, we believe in peace...*she grabs hold of the fork, and plunges it into his foot*...and a permanent end to violence...

He reels away in agony, dropping the gun...

MILLER   Get it! GET IT! *O'Hare makes a dive for the gun, picks it up and points it at Alan*...Shoot him now! Do it!

O'HARE   I will, I will...I will...

ALAN   Do it then! Because I'm not scared! I stand up for my beliefs, I fight for them and I die for them, and I don't compromise!

MILLER   Shoot the fucker!

ALAN   Do it! Martyr me and then you can write a fucking song about something that matters! About me! The second last of the Mohicans!

O'HARE   You...you...you...

ALAN   Do it!
The gun is shaking in O'Hare's hand...

O'HARE   I...

ALAN   You've no fucking backbone!

O'Hare holds the gun on Alan, but looks at Miller…

O'HARE   You do it…

MILLER   Just pull the trigger!

O'HARE   You do it! You take it!

MILLER   No! Just do it! You'll be a hero!

O'HARE   I can't…

He begins to lower the gun. Alan smiles and starts to move towards him. Sean stands and gently takes the gun..

ALAN   Ah that's my girl…

She raises the gun and pulls the trigger. There is a stunned silence as they stand looking at Alan, dead on his back. They are covered in blood.

SEAN   Molly Maguire of the Clonard Maguires despised you, and I despised you.

Miller and O'Hare look at her for a long time. Then:

O'HARE   What the fuck did you do that for?!

MILLER   You shot Snooky! First you stabbed him, then you bloody shot him.

O'HARE   You only had to wing him!

MILLER   What sort of a maniac are you?!

O'HARE   He was in a fucking badger costume!

MILLER   He was only mouthing off! They always do that!

O'HARE   You didn't have to shoot him!

MILLER   Look at him! Jesus!

O'HARE   We're fucked now, we really are fucked now...

Sean looks at them, then at the gun. She drops it. She walks to the rail of clothes and plucks off Miller's coat. She returns to Alan. When it becomes clear what she's about to do, Miller starts to say something, but stops himself. Sean puts the coat over Alan's body. She turns to them.

SEAN   You came here to do a job. Now do the fucking job!

She walks out of the room. O'Hare raises his hands in a helpless gesture and looks at Miller, open mouthed. Miller shakes his head. He gets up and slowly moves to his keyboards and sits down. He begins to pick out notes.

O'HARE   What...the fuck...are you doing?

MILLER   Working, we're here to work.

O'HARE   How can you...he...she...Christ I should never have come back...I'd forgotten what it was like...there's no hope...there's no...

Miller blasts out a power chord on the keyboard.

MILLER   No! There's a lesson here. Nothing happens for nothing!

O'HARE   What are you TALKING about?

MILLER   Don't you feel it?

O'HARE   Feel what?!

MILLER   Inspired!

O'HARE   Inspired to get on the next fucking plane...! I feel sick! We have to call...police, ambulance...

MILLER   NO! We have to use this...we have to make it work for us. If we don't get the anthem finished by five, neither of us is getting paid.

O'HARE   But he's...

MILLER   He's dead! A couple of hours isn't going to make any difference to him! We call the police as soon as we're finished.

O'HARE   We can't just...

MILLER   You need the money, and God knows I need it too...

O'HARE   You? I thought...

MILLER   The tax man is after me in seven different countries! I need this! It's the only reason I'm back in this shit hole. Okay? So get your act together and let's finish this. Do you hear me? *O'Hare is staring at Alan's body.* Dessie? I can't do it without you.

O'Hare turns to Miller.

    O'HARE   What was that?

    MILLER   I can't do it without you.

The stage goes black.

Then slowly brightens; Miller is at the keyboards, O'Hare writing furiously. O'Hare takes what he's written across to Miller, stepping over Alan's corpse. Miller reads it and nods. He begins to pick out notes. O'Hare walks back across the stage, stepping over Alan again.

The stage goes black. Then brightens.

    O'HARE   Should we order sandwiches?

Pause

    MILLER   No.

The stage goes black.

Music begins. The cast move centre stage.

    ANNOUNCER: Ladies and gentlemen, will you please be upstanding for the National Anthem.

WITH THE BLOOD OF OUR FATHERS
SPILLED UPON EV'RY STREET
WE'RE A COUNTRY DIVIDED
AND UNITED BY OUR GRIEF.
THOUGH THE FIELDS MAY BE BURNING
WITH THE FLAMES OF THE PAST
THEY'RE THE FIRES OF MY HOMELAND,
FROM THE CAUSEWAY TO BELFAST.
(Chorus)
NORTHERN IRELAND,
NORTH OF IRELAND,
NORTHERN IRELAND,
NORTH OF IRELAND.
WE'RE NORTHERN IRELAND
SO WE ARE.

(REPRISE)

THE END